PUFFIN BOOKS

Johnny Ball's Think Box

What do you need to enjoy this book? Nothing –
except a lively mind and a sense of fun.

Johnny Ball's television shows have made maths a
popular subject with children of all ages, and now, in
response to thousands of requests for more
information, he has written this marvellously
entertaining book. It's full of tricks and puzzles from
his shows, all accompanied by clear diagrams and
funny cartoons. In his lively style Johnny Ball
explains simple card and number tricks that produce
impressive results, and then proceeds to
complex-sounding tetraflexagons and
dodecahedrons, which are easier to make than to
pronounce!

You can discover Johnny Ball's rival to Rubik's
cube, some curious curves that provide a very strange
method of transport, what the ankle bones of sheep
have to do with dice and a tantalizing variety of things
to do.

This fascinating book will be enjoyed by readers of
all ages, but particularly those from ten to twelve.

D0530761

JOHNNY BALL'S

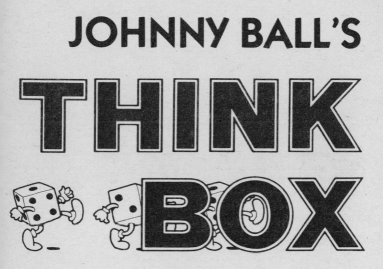

THINK BOX

Illustrated by David Woodroffe

PUFFIN BOOKS

Puffin Books, Penguin Books Ltd, Harmondsworth, Middlesex, England
Penguin Books, 625 Madison Avenue, New York, New York 10022, U.S.A.
Penguin Books Australia Ltd, Ringwood, Victoria, Australia
Penguin Books Canada Ltd, 2801 John Street, Markham, Ontario, Canada L3R 1B4
Penguin Books (N.Z.) Ltd, 182–190 Wairau Road, Auckland 10, New Zealand

First published 1982

Copyright © Johnny Ball, 1982
Illustrations copyright © David Woodroffe, 1982
All rights reserved

Set in Linotron Baskerville by
Rowland Phototypesetting Ltd,
Bury St Edmunds, Suffolk
Made and printed in Great Britain by
Cox and Wyman Ltd, Reading, Berks

Except in the United States of America, this book is sold subject
to the condition that it shall not, by way of trade or otherwise, be lent,
re-sold, hired out, or otherwise circulated without the
publisher's prior consent in any form of binding or cover other than
that in which it is published and without a similar condition
including this condition being imposed on the subsequent purchaser

CONTENTS

Introduction   9

1 As easy as counting on your fingers   11
2 Fantastic figuring   18
3 Good old card tricks   27
4 Getting wrapped up in paper   37
5 You can do it with your eyes closed   51
6 Paper, plane and simple   61
7 Nimble number tricks   79
8 Timely tricks and date-divining   89
9 Tricks with odds and ends   103
10 Solid, man, solid   122
11 Things to make you think   147
   Index   158

This book is dedicated to Martin Gardner for his inspiration, Albert Barber, 'Think' programme producer, for his loyalty, and my wife, Dianne, for her patience.

INTRODUCTION

It's now about four years since the first 'Think of a Number' programme was broadcast on BBC TV and since then there have been several spin-off series: 'Think Again', 'Think Backwards' and our latest effort, 'Think This Way'

Altogether, there have been around fifty programmes, each packed with puzzles and tricks and ideas which, apart from being fun, have also made maths and science that much easier to understand.

Each time a 'Think' programme appears on television the BBC is inundated with letters asking for explanations and solutions and more information. Well, here it is in one volume – the full collection of 'Think' tricks and puzzles. I hope you find it interesting and fascinating, but most of all . . . fun.

Cheers,

CHAPTER 1

As easy as counting on your fingers

A lot of people have the impression that to enjoy a book about number tricks and puzzles, you need to be fairly good at maths. What a load of tosh. (That's a rubbish word for 'rubbish'.) With this book, it doesn't really matter. All the items that follow are easy and should help you to relax and have fun with numbers and number ideas. In fact, the less you know already, the more there is to enjoy in this book – and you might even learn a few things.

The first thing to learn with maths is that you have to relax and not worry if things go wrong at first. Take the simple sum below. It's only simple addition but you must do it exactly as I say. Cover the sum with your hand or a piece of paper, then reveal one number at a time and add as you go: one thousand plus twenty is one thousand and twenty, plus thirty is one thousand and fifty, and so on. OK? Well, go on then. Try it! Quick!

$$
\begin{array}{r}
1000 \\
+ \quad 20 \\
+ \quad 30 \\
+ \quad 1000 \\
+ \quad 1030 \\
+ \quad 1000 \\
+ \quad 20 \\
\hline
\\
\hline
\end{array}
$$

OK? What answer did you get? Was it 5000? Well, if you did, join the club. Over 90 per cent of people who try this sum get 5000 for the answer. Trouble is – it's wrong. The correct answer is 4100.

Most people go wrong just at the end where you have to add 4080 and 20. Because there have been no hundreds mentioned in the sum, they tend to carry the one over to the thousands column and get 5000 by mistake.

So you see, if you got it wrong, don't worry; you're in the majority. If you got it right, congratulations! You have won a special star prize!*!*!* A Free Walk to Penzance*!*!*!*!*

Whether you got that sum right or wrong, I put it in first because it is a very good weapon to have in your mathematical armoury. Now when you meet someone who is really hot at maths, you can try this sum on them. Chances are they will get it wrong and that will bring them down a gentle peg or two.

Next, you need to boost your own power at maths. It's easy really because every new mathematical principle has been devised to make things easier, and there's nothing easier than counting on your fingers. Great things, fingers. They're always handy. I keep mine in my pockets so that I know where they are if I want them quickly.

Multiplying by nine

First, hold out your hands palms upwards, like this and imagine your fingers are numbered 1 to 10 from left to right.

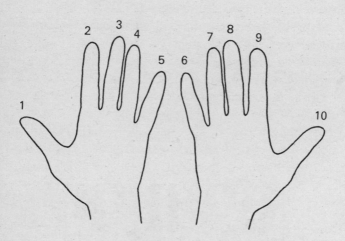

Now, if you want to multiply any single figure by nine, it's easier than twiddling your thumbs. Say you want to multiply 9 × 5. Simply fold down the finger numbered 5 (that's the little finger on your left hand). You should have four fingers sticking up to the left of this little finger and five to the right of it – and the answer is forty-five: 9 × 5 = 45.

This trick is very old hat and appears in almost every puzzle book. But why does it work? It works because 9 is our highest single figure and one less than our base number. (There are ten basic numbers in our number system, so it is called the Base Ten System.) Take a look

at your nine times table. Each product is made up of
two digits that add up to nine.

$$1 \times 9 = 9$$
$$2 \times 9 = 18 \ (1 + 8 = 9)$$
$$3 \times 9 = 27 \ (2 + 7 = 9)$$

. . . and so on.

If you fold down one of your ten fingers, you are left
with nine sticking up, so the trick works.

The Chinese abacus

This is the ancient Chinese calculator and you can use
one hand to explain how it works.

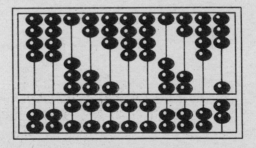

An abacus has two sets of beads: one set in fours and
another set in ones, or more often, twos. Each row is just
like the fingers on your right hand. Your fingers represent the four beads and your thumb the other beads.
Your hand can represent the basic ten numbers like
this:

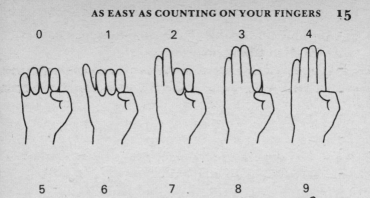

Using two hands, you can now compute all the numbers from 0 to 99.

If you really want to compute on your fingers, why not do it the same way computers do it? Computers use binary numbers – numbers in Base Two. This means that only two numbers are used: 0 and 1. To count in binary on your fingers, it is best to count from the right, so here goes. Hands out, palms upwards. Imagine your fingers are numbered like this:

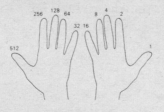

Here are a few examples on just the right hand to show how numbers can be expressed:

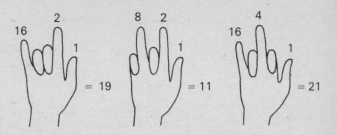

With all your fingers and thumbs extended, you will be showing:

$$512 + 256 + 128 + 64 + 32 + 16 + 8 + 4 + 2 + 1 = 1023$$

and it is possible to represent every number up to and including 1023 on just two hands.

If you want to perform calculation feats which are extra mind-boggling, as well as finger-tangling, why not try calculating in the tertiary or Base Three System. For this, each finger or thumb needs three positions – down, bent in the middle and straight. The fingers would be numbered like this:

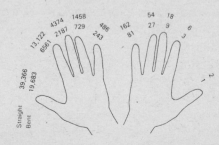

The first eight numbers would be expressed on just the first finger and thumb of the right hand like this:

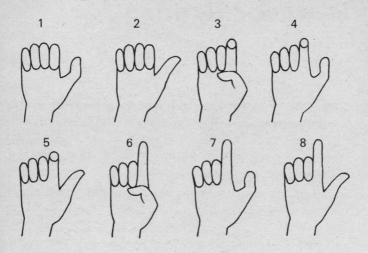

It is complicated but it's amazing how, with just a little practice, you can get your fingers to stay in all sorts of positions. Using this system, you can represent every number up to and including 59,048 – all on two bunches of five.

How's this for 1982?

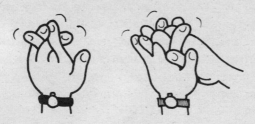

CHAPTER 2

Fantastic figuring

Do you know what a 'funambulist' is? According to my dictionary, it's someone who does amazing tricks on a rope. A tightrope-walker. Perhaps someone who does amazing tricks with numbers could be called a 'funumberist' or a 'funumerist'. However, many people are more scared of playing with numbers than they would be walking a tightrope. That's silly really because numbers are much safer and ever so easy to get along with once you know how. For instance, here is a mind-boggling trick that, with the aid of a pocket calculator, you can do in five seconds flat (or even five seconds bumpy).

Say to someone, 'Give me any two-digit number and I will tell you the total of all the numbers from one, up to and including that number.' As an example, if he were to give you 76, you would come up with the answer 2926 in about five seconds.

This trick is pretty impressive and yet it is so simple. In fact, it was invented by a six-year-old boy, although I must admit he turned out to be a genius. His name was Karl Friedrich Gauss (say it like house with a 'g') and he was six years old just two hundred years ago. One day his teacher asked him to add up all the numbers from 1 to 10. Karl immediately thought $1 + 10 = 11$. Then he realized that $2 + 9 = 11$ and $3 + 8 = 11$

and $4 + 7 = 11$ and $5 + 6 = 11$. Now that gives us five pairs that make 11, and $5 \times 11 = 55$, and that's the answer.

Young Karl didn't stop there. 'What about adding all the numbers to 100?' he thought. OK.

Add the first and last numbers to
  find what each pair will make: $1 + 100 =$ 101
One hundred numbers would split
  into fifty pairs: $100 \div 2 =$ 50
Therefore the answer is: $101 \times 50 = 5050$

Easy, isn't it? Now you know the formula, you can perform the trick for any number you like. Take an example: what is the total of all the numbers from 1 to 76?

Add the first and last numbers to
  find what each pair will
  make: $1 + 76 =$ 77
Divide by 2 to find the number of
  pairs: $76 \div 2 =$ 38
The answer is: $77 \times 38 = 2926$

With odd numbers the method is slightly different. Try 77. You can work this out on your calculator.

First enter the number: 77
Divide by 2 to find the number of
  pairs: $77 \div 2 =$ 38.5
Get rid of any remainder by
  rounding up to the next
  whole number: 39
The answer is: $77 \times 39 = 3003$

So there you are. With a bit of practice you'll be as good at the trick as Karl Friedrich Gauss, but whether people will think you're a genius . . . your gauss is as good as mine.

```
UHHHHHH. . .
```

While you have your calculator handy, here's another trick you can try. Most people find division one of the most difficult things to do in maths. Dividing by 2, 3, 4 and 5 isn't so bad. The trouble lies in dividing by numbers like 7, 11 or 13 – am I right? Well, how's this for a trick? I'll get you to punch a six-figure number into your calculator that I guarantee will be divisible by 7, 11 and 13, all at the same time. OK?

Think of any three-figure number and punch it into your calculator. Right, now punch the same number in again. So, if you thought of 367, you should end up with the six-figure number 367367. There, that's all there is to it. Now for the test:

Try dividing it by 7. Any remainder? No? Good.
Now divide the new number by 11. Any remainder? No. Amazing.
Now divide this new number by 13. Any remainder? No! Astonishing!
Now to cap it all, what number are you left with? Well, would you believe it. It's the three-figure number you first thought of.

Why and how does it work? Well, multiply any three-figure number by 1001 and you get the same three figures repeated. 367 × 1001 = 367367. Also, if you multiply 7 × 11 × 13 the answer is 1001. So dividing 367367 by 7 then 11 then 13 is the same as dividing the sum by 1001 and the answer must be 367. Try it with a few alternatives. It works every time.

The great thing about pocket calculators is that they have taken away the drudgery of maths calculations so that today we can tackle quite complex mathematical tricks fairly easily. In olden days there were very few short cuts in calculation, but the short cuts that were used make very interesting tricks today.

Russian multiplication

It was said that the people in ancient Russia were very poor at maths. They could double a number or halve it but they couldn't multiply or divide and they didn't know anything about fractions. So how did they manage when they needed to multiply two numbers together?

Take, for example, 36 × 27. A pocket calculator will tell you that the answer is 972. This is how the Russians tackled the problem:

First they would write the numbers side by side:	36	27
Then they would halve the left-hand number and write the answer underneath:	18	
They would repeat this process: but if they got an answer ending in ½ they would cross it off:	9	
	4½	
	2	
Eventually they would get to:	1	

HIM A RUSSIAN

Then they would start to *double* the number on the right so they had two columns of figures side by side like this:

$$
\begin{array}{cc}
36 & 27 \\
18 & 54 \\
9 & 108 \\
4\cancel{\tfrac{1}{2}} & 216 \\
2 & 432 \\
1 & 864 \\
\end{array}
$$

Now apparently the Russians were always having purges, which means getting rid of things. One thing they couldn't stand was even numbers on the left-hand side. If they found any even number on the left, they would purge or cross out that whole line. So the two columns of figures would look like this:

even	~~36~~	~~27~~
even	~~18~~	~~54~~
odd	9	108
even	~~4½~~	~~216~~
even	~~2~~	~~432~~
odd	1	864

The total of the numbers left in the right-hand column is

$$972$$

This is the right answer, but it makes you think. When it came to doing multiplication, there was no rushin' a Russian.

Elizabethan multiplication

In the days of Good Queen Bess very few people would have admitted that arithmetic was their strong point. However, they did develop a way of multiplying big numbers for people who had only learnt to multiply numbers less than 10. It was all achieved using an arrangement of squares which were then divided into triangles. As an example, let's say they needed to multiply 367 × 193. A pocket calculator will tell you the answer is 70831.

The Elizabethans would lay the numbers out as shown in the diagram on the next page. The numbers they wanted to multiply were written across the top and down one side. They then multiplied each figure across the top with each figure down the side. The results were entered in the appropriate triangle. Then the whole thing was added up diagonally to get the answer.

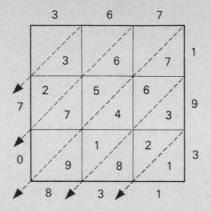

Now if you turn the grid system in the diagram above onto its corner, you can produce some fascinating number patterns. Take the sum 555 × 555 = 308025.

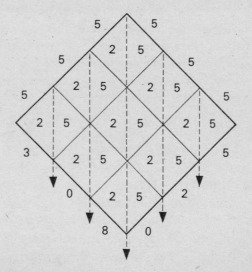

Once you understand how it works, you can generate patterns without the grid. Try 66666 × 88888. All you need to know is that there are five digits in each of these numbers and that 6 × 8 = 48. You need a diamond of 48s that is five 48s wide at its widest point.

```
                4 8
              4 8 4 8
            4 8 4 8 4 8
          4 8 4 8 4 8 4 8
        4 8 4 8 4 8 4 8 4 8
          4 8 4 8 4 8 4 8
            4 8 4 8 4 8
              4 8 4 8
                4 8
```

$$5\ 9\ 2\ 5\ 8\ 0\ 7\ 4\ 0\ 8$$

Another way to do the same sum is to write a diamond of 6s like this:

```
            6
          6   6
        6   6   6
      6   6   6   6
    6   6   6   6   6
      6   6   6   6
        6   6   6
          6   6
            6
```

Add it up: 740725926

Then multiply by 8 as shown on the next page.

This can be condensed into a triangle of 6s that is five rows deep.

$$
\begin{array}{c}
6 \\
666 \\
66666 \\
6666666 \\
666666666
\end{array}
$$

Add it up: 740725926

Multiply by 8: ×8

5925807408

Same answer – different pattern.

CHAPTER 3

Good old card tricks

There is very little new about card tricks because there is nothing new about playing cards. They have been around for a long time. They most probably began as a sort of ancient Chinese or Korean 'Monopoly' money. Paper money appeared in the East some 1300 years ago and people gambled with it, until someone invented paper notes especially for gambling with. It is believed that these notes developed into playing cards.

The fifty-two-card pack came into use about five-hundred years ago. King Henry VIII banned the playing of cards except at Christmas because cards were held to be sinful and evil. At Christmas in 1529, Bishop Latimer gave special Card Sermons where he likened the cards to the Bible and the almanac – the twelve picture cards representing the twelve disciples, the suits representing the four apostles, fifty-two cards for the weeks in a year, and so on. A modern version of this can be heard in the 'Deck of Cards', a Country and Western song still broadcast from time to time.

If cards are old, so are many of the tricks that are performed with them. The art of being a good magician lies in dressing up old tricks in new and entertaining ways. The tricks which follow do not involve any of the secret effects that magicians use, like hiding cards up sleeves or rabbits up your jumper. All these tricks involve some mathematical principle and actually work themselves. Try them and see.

As many as you...

First place a pack of cards in front of someone and ask her to take *a few*. (Don't ask 'her' if it's a 'him'. This time round I'm going to assume it's a 'her'.) Then you take some as well, but make sure you take quite a few *more than she took*. Ask her to count her cards secretly and while she is doing that, you count your cards. Let's suppose you took 20 cards. Split that number into two numbers, one of which must still be bigger than her total. Let's say you choose 16 and 4.

Now you say, 'I don't know how many cards you took, but I bet I have as many as you plus 4, plus enough to make yours up to 16.' Ask her to count her cards out onto the table. Let's assume she had 10. You say, 'I bet I have as many as you.' (Deal out 10 of your cards.)

'Plus 4 . . .' (Deal out 4 cards.)

'Plus enough to make your cards up to 16.' (Deal your remaining cards onto her 10 saying, '11, 12, 13, 14, 15, 16.')

All you have done is to count out your 20 cards in a tricky and confusing way, but when you look at your helper's face, you'll see that she is both puzzled and amazed!

Red and black, red and black

Take a pack of cards and sort them out so they are arranged alternately red and black. Show the audience how the pack is arranged. Then ask someone to 'cut' the cards and to give them one 'riffle-shuffle'.

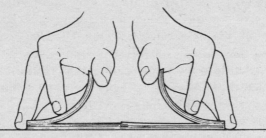

Take the cards back and thumb through them to show the audience that they are now mixed up. They will see several instances of two red or two black cards together. Now, you perform the trick . . .

As you are showing the cards, select any pair of cards of the same colour and separate the pack between these two cards. Bring the bottom half of the pack to the top and turn the cards face down again.

The audience have just seen the mixed-up pack so they will be totally stupefied when you start dealing the cards in pairs from the top of the pack because *each pair will contain one red and one black card*. It works like magic!

The four~suit swindle

This trick is a more complex version of the previous trick. First sort out the pack so that you have heart, club, diamond, spade in that order all the way through the pack. Show the audience what you have done. Ask someone to take the pack and deal the cards face down one at a time in a pile until he is about halfway through the pack. Point out to him that he now has one pile in strict suit order and one pile in the same order, only reversed.

Ask him to destroy that order by riffle-shuffling the two piles together. When this is done, turn the pack over and thumb through it proving that the cards have indeed been mixed up. While you are doing this, look for two cards of the same suit together and cut the pack between these two cards. Bring the bottom half to the top and turn the pack face down again.

The audience know the cards are mixed up because they have seen it with their own eyes, so now you bamboozle them by dealing the cards in fours from the top of the pack. The first time you do it you will stagger yourself when you see that every four cards contains one heart, one club, one diamond and one spade.

Wrong way up

To perform this trick you need a pack of cards and two chairs and a table. If you like, you can borrow these items as it isn't worth the expense of buying a table and chairs just for one trick.

First sit at the table with the person who is going to help you do the trick. Give her the pack of cards and ask her to turn eight cards the wrong way up and shuffle them into the pack. Now ask her to hold the cards under the table and deal the top eight cards into her free hand and pass them to you – still under the table.

Next you say, 'I have supersensory bionic fingers which can feel the difference between the back of the cards and the fronts. I also have X-ray vision and can see into the pack you have in your hands. From this information I can deduce that there are exactly the same number of cards the wrong way up in my hands as there are in your hands.'

You now produce your cards and count those which are the wrong way up. Ask your helper to go through her cards and count her 'wrong-way-up' cards. Surprise, surprise! You both have the same number the wrong way up. How does it work?

All you need to do is this. As your helper hands you the eight cards you simply turn them over in your hands before you bring them from under the table.

I'll try to explain how the trick works. If your eight cards contain no face-up cards, then the rest of the pack must contain eight. By turning yours over, you now have eight the wrong way up. If your eight cards contain two face-up cards, the rest of the pack will contain six. By turning your eight over, you will also have six the wrong way up. So it works every time!

The magic square

This trick begins with nine cards set in a magic square. (The square is magic because each row, column and diagonal adds up to 15, but that has nothing to do with the trick.) For effect, use red cards for all the numbers except the 5 in the middle which can be black.

You need a coin or counter or upturned glass to move from card to card, and a specially prepared instruction card in an envelope. (More of this later.) Explain to your helper, 'I am going to ask you to place this object on any card you choose. Then I will take the card from this envelope which will give you instructions to remove a card and move the object so many steps from card to card. You may only move up, down or sideways – not diagonally. If the instructions ask you to move two steps, you may reverse your path. Thus, if you are on card 6, two steps could take you to 8, 5 or 2 or back to 6. OK? The instructions will continue until there is only one card left. Here is the magic part. I guarantee that you will finish on the black 5.'

Before you continue, make sure that the instructions are understood. This applies to you too! Ask your helper to place the object on the card of her choice. Let's assume she chooses card number 6. You remove the card from the envelope and ask her to follow these instructions.

Remove card 7.
Move five steps and remove card 8.
Move four steps and remove card 2.
Move six steps and remove card 4.
Move three steps and remove card 9.
Move two steps and remove card 3.
Move one step and remove card 6.
Move three steps and remove card 1 (the ace).

'Your object is now on the only remaining card – the black number 5.'

The effect is quite stunning, but how does it work? Well, those instructions would have produced the same results if your helper had started on any of the corner cards or the centre card. But if she had started on card 1, 3, 7 or 9 another set of instructions would have been needed and these instructions are written on the back of the instruction card.

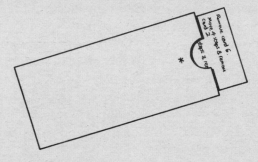

Remove card 6.
Move four steps and remove card 2.
Move five steps and remove card 1.
Move three steps and remove card 4.
Move one step and remove card 7.
Move two steps and remove card 9.
Move five steps and remove card 8.
Move three steps and remove card 3.

'Your object is now on the only remaining card – the black number 5.'

The only bit of trickery needed in this trick is in marking the envelope so that you know which set of instructions will be showing when you remove the card . . . Remove the card only when your helper has chosen her starting position and you have got the envelope the right way up. This way, the magic square will work every time.

The six-card trick

This is one of my favourite card tricks. It is very effective and yet it is so simple to perform because it works itself. You start with six cards laid out like this:

3 black backs and 3 clubs

Explain to your helper that you want him to guess which one of the cards is a 'red' one. You then produce an invisible die like the one in the picture . . .

(Die is the singular of dice, but most people never use the word. The expression 'Never say die' has got nothing to do with it either . . .) Ask your helper to roll the die and tell you the number on the top face. (He'll probably think you're off your trolley, but in most cases it will be done just to humour you.) Let's assume he says the number showing is 3. You simply count three cards from the left and turn that card over. Sure enough, it's the five of hearts (see below). You now turn over the other two face-down cards to reveal the three of clubs and the six of clubs. So, your helper has chosen the red card as predicted.

Now, that's all very well, but what if he chose the number 4? Simple. All you do is count four cards along, but from the right. That way you still arrive at the five of hearts. What if he chose number 5? You turn over each of the face down cards revealing that the only red card is the five of hearts, so the trick works that way too.

Unless your IQ is in single figures, you'll be wondering what happens if 1, 2 or 6 are chosen. Right?? Right!! The secret lies in the two of clubs at one end. It happens to be one card along from the right and also six cards along from the left and also the only number 2. In either case you turn over the ace and the four to reveal black backs and then you turn over the two to reveal . . .? Have you guessed? A red back. In setting up the trick, you need to take the two of clubs from a different pack – a pack with *red backs*.

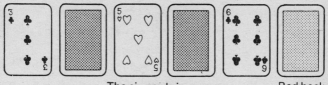

The six cards in reverse   Red back

This type of trick is called a 'get-out' trick because, for any possible occurrence, there is always a get-out. I hope what you get out of these tricks is – fun!

CHAPTER 4

Getting wrapped up in paper

First you will need a pen or pencil, a ruler, a pair of scissors and some sticky tape.

Oh, yes – I nearly forgot – some paper. A4 will do (297 × 210mm).

If you examine a piece of paper, you will find that it has two sides (one on each side) but only one edge which runs all the way round it. That doesn't seem fair, does it? If it's got two sides, why can't it have two edges? Well, it can have two edges if you cut a hole in it. In fact, if you cut a lot of holes in it, it can have as many edges as you like. However, no matter how many holes you give your piece of paper, it will always have just two sides (on opposite sides).

Now, here's a question. Can a piece of paper have more than two sides? Well, yes it can if you curl it up to form two loops, rather like the letter S in a circle. This shape has an outside and two separate insides.

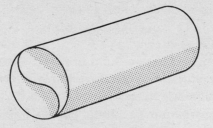

By adding more and more curls to the paper, you can form as many sides as you like.

Now here's a tricky question. Can a piece of paper have just ONE side? Sounds impossible, doesn't it? But try this. Cut a strip of paper about 2cm wide and 30cm long. The strip has two sides and one edge. If you form it into a simple loop it will suddenly have two sides and two edges.

Right, now this time form a loop, but before you join the two ends together, give the strip a half twist and then join the ends with sticky tape.

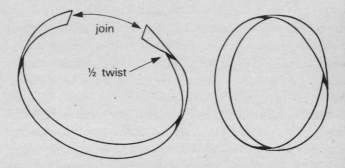

Take a pencil and make a mark near one edge of your loop. Now, carefully let your finger trace its way round the edge of the loop and see what happens . . . You will find that your finger comes back to where it started which means that your loop has only one edge.

Now try this. Put the loop on the table and let your pencil rest on it. Then slowly pull the loop along under the pencil so that the pencil draws a line along the centre of the loop. What happens? You will find that when you have gone once round the loop, your pencil (amazingly!) will be on the other side of the paper from where it started. If you keep going round, you will find that the pencil always comes back to where it started from, which means that you have created a piece of paper with only one edge and only one side. What you have created is called a Möbius Band which seems to have been discovered by August Ferdinand Möbius, a German mathematician, around 1858. What good is it? It's good fun. Try this.

Get your scissors and cut your Möbius Band along the line you have drawn, but before you do it, try to guess what shape you will end up with. Normally when you cut something down the middle, you end up with two pieces, but with the Möbius Band you get one band twice as long as the one you started with. What's more, whereas it had one side and one edge and one twist in it, now it has two sides and two edges and two twists in it. Mind-bending, innit?

Here's something else you can try with a Möbius Band. You'll have to make another one first. You've just cut the one you had in half . . . although it's not in half!?!?!? Anyway, this time take your band and start to cut along it one third of the way in from the edge.

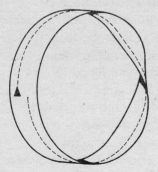

Notice what happens. When you have gone round the band once you come to the place you started from but your cut has moved another third of the way across the band. Keep going and try to guess the shape you'll end up with before you finish cutting. You'll find that the band is in two pieces but both are different. First you have a band just like the one you started with except that it is only a third of its original width, and this band is looped up with another band twice as long with two sides, two edges and two twists.

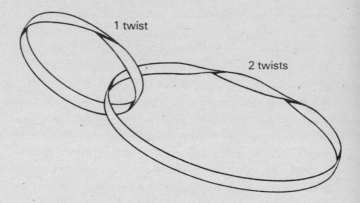

1 twist

2 twists

Don't throw it away. Here comes the tricky bit . .

Take your pencil and shade or mark all round the shorter band so that you can tell it from the longer band. Now with a bit of effort, you will be able to assemble the two bands to form a single band three layers thick. You may find this frustrating to do, but try hard. You will find that the middle layer is your shaded one. Now, show it to someone and ask them how many bands there are. On seeing the shaded one in the middle, they will be certain that there must be three.

How can a band be sandwiched between *one* band? Let them unravel it and they will see the truth. Now tell them to reassemble it . . .

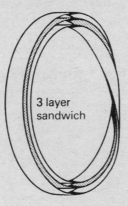

3 layer
sandwich

While they are struggling with that little problem, here's one for you to struggle with. Make two paper loops and stick them together as shown.

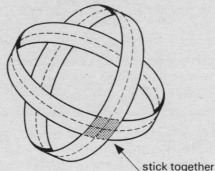

stick together
at this point only

These loops have no kinks or twists in them so you

should be able to imagine what form they will take when you cut them both in half lengthways (along the dotted line). Can you guess? Cut them in half and see. I bet you're surprised at the result.

How to make a Tetratetraflexagon

Flexagons are fings – sorry – things which flex or fold to reveal hidden faces. Tetraflexagons have four sides, but they can be made with three, four or six faces. Let's start with a four-faced flexagon. It's called a Tetratetraflexagon!

Take an oblong piece of paper and divide it into twelve squares as shown here.

Number the squares as shown or you can substitute colours or different shading if you wish. When you have done that, mark up the back of the paper like this.

Back

When that's done, turn the paper over and cut along the dotted line. This forms a 'door' which you fold backwards. Fold the right-hand side of the paper along line A–B and then fold again along line C–D.

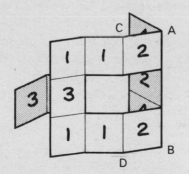

Fold the 'door' over to the front and stick down with sellotape. You should have a rectangle made up of six squares with the figure 1 in each square.

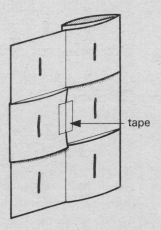

tape

Turn it over and you should see six 2s. Fold the flexagon backwards and you'll find a new face with either six 3s or a new colour on it. Fold this face backwards and you'll find the fourth face. If a four-faced flexagon tickles your fancy, stand by because here comes a six-faced flexagon!

A six-faced tetraflexagon is called a Hexatetra-flexagon. Start with a square piece of paper which you need to fold to form sixteen squares. Cut out the middle four squares as you won't be needing them. Snip through the dotted line and number the front and back of the square like this.

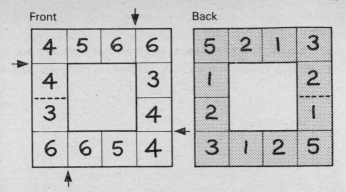

With the front facing you, fold the paper forwards along the four lines marked with arrows. Keep folding the paper forwards until you have the shape shown below. Fold it forwards again at arrow 1, backwards at arrow 2 and back again at arrow 3.

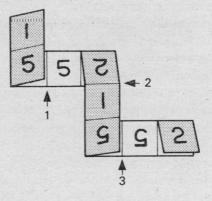

Tuck one flap behind so you have four 2s in front and four 1s behind. Finally, wrap a small piece of sellotape over the top as shown.

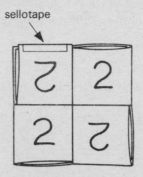

sellotape

This flexagon folds like a book but in two different directions – horizontally and vertically. Now you have the problem of flexing to find all six faces!

How to make a Hexahexaflexagon!!

Hexaflexagons differ from tetraflexagons in that they have six sides instead of four. This particular hexaflexagon also has six faces which makes it a Hexahexaflexagon. You can make it any size you like, but the measurements used here are ideal if you use A4-size paper (297 × 210mm).

Position the paper on its long side and mark it off from the bottom left corner. The first mark is 1.5cm along and the other marks follow at 3cm intervals, right to the other end. Go back to your first mark and draw a line exactly 3cm long connecting it with the left-hand edge of the paper. From the top of this line, draw a line parallel to the marked edge and mark it off at 3cm intervals. By joining up your marks you should make a strip containing nineteen triangles. (The last one will have a corner missing, but don't worry.)

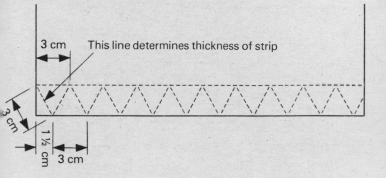

Cut the strip out and mark it up on both sides as shown below.

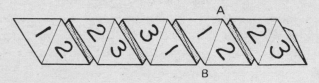

Now fold your strip so that the same underside numbers come together. It should look like this:

Fold this shape back along line A–B and then back again along line C–D.

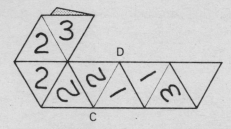

Arrange it so that you have six 2s showing and one triangle marked 1 sticking up. Fold this triangle over and stick the two blank faces together. The side opposite the 2s should show six 1s. Your Hexahexaflexagon is now ready for flexing.

Pinch two triangles together as if you were folding the whole thing in half. Then push down the opposite point and the flexagon will take the shape of a three-winged dart flight. The flexagon will now separate in the middle like a flower opening to reveal another face. Two more flexes will bring you back to the start. By pinching two other faces, you will discover another face and, by trial and error, you will find there are six different faces.

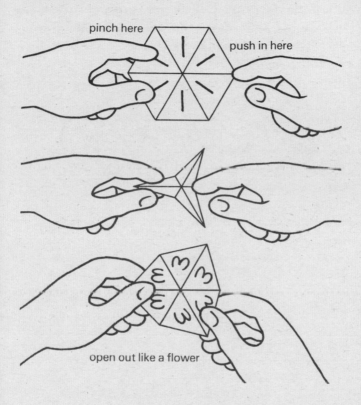

pinch here

push in here

open out like a flower

If you really get hooked on hexaflexagons, it is possible to make them with any number of faces you like. However, the folding gets very complicated. For a twelve-faced hexaflexagon you start with a strip containing thirty-seven triangles. If you fold it as shown on page 47, that will give you a nineteen-triangle strip and then you proceed as with the Hexahexaflex-agon. You can number the faces 7–12 after you have made it. When you have made your flexagon you could pattern the faces instead of numbering them. If you do complete this task, you will be the owner of a Dodecahexaflexagon!!!!

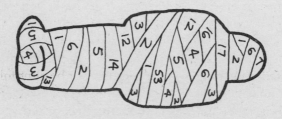

CHAPTER 5

You can do it with your eyes closed

All the tricks in this chapter are so easy, you can do them with your eyes closed, but don't close them yet or you won't be able to read the instructions. If you try to perform these tricks with your eyes closed, you may be accused of peeping, so turn your back or be blindfolded. You could even nip down to the nearest call box and do the tricks by phone. Whatever the case, when you try these tricks on your friends, you'll open their eyes, but they'll still be in the dark as to how the tricks work. Here's the first one . . .

Three piles of matches (or paper clips)

First you need three spaces marked A, B and C and an ordinary max of botches, sorry, bax of motches – er, mox of batches . . . It would be safer with paper clips.

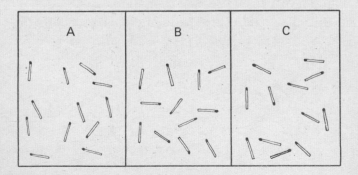

Turn your back or close your eyes or arrange yourself so that you can't see what's going on. Now ask your helper to make three piles of paper clips or whatever you're using. Ask him to make sure there are the same number of items in each pile. Next, ask him to move three items from pile A to pile B and then to discard (that means chuck away) the rest of pile A.

Ask him to take three items from pile C and add them to pile B. Now ask him to count the remainder in pile C and to take that number from pile B. This all sounds confusing, but really the trick is now complete because, in a crafty way, you have ensured that pile B now contains three sets of three, or a total of nine items.

You can further complicate the trick by asking your helper to split pile B into two piles and to hand you either pile. (If you're doing this by phone, ask him to tell you the number in one pile.) Take this number away from nine and you will know the number in the remaining pile.

When I performed this trick on television, I asked for the remainder to be placed on a balanced seesaw and explained that by holding the other end of the seesaw I could feel the difference in pressure. However, I had been handed four matches, so although I was blindfolded, I knew that there had to be five matches on the seesaw. The chat about pressure was just a noad of lonsense – sorry, I mean a rot of lubbish.

Coins on a clock face

To prepare for this trick, draw a circular clock face and place a coin on each number from 1 to 12. The coins needn't be the same, but make sure they are all head-side up. (Last Christmas at home, I tried this trick with chocolate coins, but while I was blindfolded my kids made them all disappear.)

Right. Now turn your back and ask someone to turn over any six coins she likes. When she has done this, ask her to turn six coins over for you – those on numbers 1, 4, 5, 8, 9 and 10. You have to remember these numbers, but make it sound as though you're choosing them at random. Explain that some of them may be coins that she has already turned over, but to turn them over again. Ask her now to count the number of heads and tell you the answer. She will give you an even-numbered answer from 0 to 12. There is just a chance that she will call 0 or 12. This means that you chose either the six numbers she chose or the six that she didn't choose. Either way, it will seem like a miracle, so stop the trick there and say, 'Here's a similar trick,' and start again.

If she calls an even number from 2 to 10, you now explain that you are going to divide the coins into two piles, each containing exactly half the heads. Ask her to slide the following coins into the centre of the face: the coins showing the times five to twelve, ten-past seven and quarter-past six. On turning round you will see that half the heads are in the centre and half are on the outer ring.

To understand how the trick works, it is best to do it

backwards. First set up the coins as for the start of the trick. Then slide to the middle the coins showing five to twelve, ten-past seven and quarter-past six. Now turn over those coins on numbers 1, 4, 5, 8, 9 and 10. You can see that what you have done is to move six coins to the middle and turn the others over.

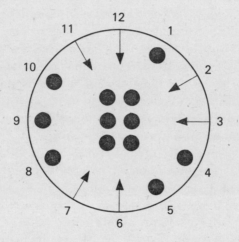

If you now turn six coins over, no matter which six you choose, you will be left with two identical sets. Perform the trick the right way round and it is very difficult to see how it is done. So this clock-face trick works itself and leaves your audience with puzzled faces.

Choose an object

First you need to collect together several items. For example, a pen, a book, a ruler, a pencil, a gluepot and a teaspoon. Notice anything unusual? Each item has a different number of letters in its name. You must tell your audience what each object is so that they call it by its proper name.

Next, turn your back or have yourself blindfolded and ask someone to select an object and show it to everyone else. Ask him to write down its name and count the letters. Ask him now to multiply the number by 5 and add 3. Now ask him to double it. Then ask him to find someone else who will whisper in his ear a number from 1 to 10. This number he is told to add to the total. Tell him that your supersensory hearing could pick up the noise of the object being lifted, the number of letters written down and even the whispered number.

You now ask for the total he has calculated and immediately you can tell him both the object he chose and the number that was whispered. How? Well, it's simple and it has nothing to do with supersensory hearing.

Suppose he chose the pencil. The trick would go like this:

Count the letters in PENCIL:	6
Multiply by 5:	30
Add 3:	33
Double it:	66
Add the whispered number (say 7):	73

When you hear him call out 73 you take away twice the number you first added ($3 \times 2 = 6$). So $73 - 6 = 67$. So you know the object chosen had 6 letters in its name and the whispered number was 7.

This is just a complicated way of doing a simple 'Think of a number' trick, but it's a lot more entertaining, don't you think?

Three-object divination

This is a complicated name for what is really a very simple trick. All you need are three everyday objects. When I did the trick on television, the theme of the show had been water so I used a rubber fish, a rubber duck and a bar of soap. (It was soap soap, not rubber soap.)

First place the objects on a piece of paper with positions marked 1, 2 and 3.

Then give these instructions to your helper: 'Here are three everyday objects. In a moment I am going to turn my back and I want you to swap the position of any two objects, but as you do it, I want you to shout the position numbers like this.' (Demonstrate a couple of times swapping over two items and calling the numbers out, until your helper understands.) The important moment is just before you turn round!

Just imagine that the first three fingers on your right hand are numbered 1, 2 and 3. Then look down and remember the positions of one of the objects. Let's say it's the soap on position 3. Touch your third finger with your thumb and keep it there. OK. Now turn your back.

Ask your helper to start swapping and calling out the numbers. Listen carefully because you are listening for a 3. If your helper shouts 2 and 3, you know that she has swapped the soap from position 3 to position 2, so you do the same with your thumb. Swap it to your second finger.

You are now listening for a 2. If she shouts 2 and 1, swap the thumb to the finger number 1. If you are touching 1 and she calls 2 and 3 just leave your thumb where it is. Carry on until she has had enough and stops. Now you say, 'Right, they're pretty mixed up. Now, just to fool me, I want you to take two objects and swap them over, but this time don't tell me which two you are swapping. OK?' When she has done this, you turn round to look at the objects.

Your thumb is still touching one of your fingers. Let's assume it is finger number 1. Look at position 1. If the soap is there you know that she must have swapped 2 and 3. If the soap is in any other position, she must have swapped the soap with the object now in position 1. Everyone will be amazed that you can magically tell which were the last two objects touched, and yet it's so simple when you know how, isn't it?

Dicey deception

It's surprising how traditional games seem to rise and decline in popularity time and time again. For example, the game of backgammon can be traced back well over 2000 years, but when I was at school I had never heard of it. Today, however, there is a back-gammon set in most homes, and once again the game is enjoying tremendous popularity.

Backgammon is played with four dice and whenever I see a backgammon set I am always tempted to do this four-dice trick. Try it. It's so easy you can do it with your eyes closed.

Give someone the four backgammon dice and ask him to form them into a tower while you turn your back.

Now point out that the dots on the sides of the dice can be seen and could be added up quickly to perform a trick. You, however, are not going to do this. You are going to add up the faces that cannot be seen, even by the person who built the tower and you are going to do it by using deep concentration.

Ask your helper to look carefully at the face at the bottom of the tower – the one face-down on the table. Now ask him to add on all the faces that are touching, namely those between the first and second dice, the two between the second and third dice and the two between the third and fourth dice. Ask him to concentrate on that total. You now turn round and almost immediately tell him that total.

How is it done? When you turn round you simply note the number on the face on the top of the tower and you subtract it from 28 to give the answer. The reason this works is that on a normal die, opposite faces always add up to 7. In working the trick you have got your helper to add four pairs of opposite faces with the exception of the top face. $4 \times 7 = 28$, and, in our example, $28 - 4 = 24$. OK? Now you can get on with the game of backgammon.

YES, I THINK THAT'S PLAIN

CHAPTER 6

Paper, plane and simple

This chapter is supposed to be about simple things you can do with a plain piece of paper. Unfortunately we spelt 'plain' (meaning flat) wrongly at the top of the page. That 'plane' is the flying variety and this chapter is not about that sort of plane.

The trouble is, some of you having read 'Paper, plane and simple' will now be disappointed that there is no plane in this chapter. You may even be near to tears . . . Oh, all right – stop blubbering. Just to keep you happy I'll throw in a design for a paper plane made from plain paper.

Take a piece of plain paper and cut three strips about 5cm wide. Roll one strip into a long thin tube and stick it together with sellotape. Make the other two strips into hoops, one slightly smaller than the other and fasten them with sellotape. Then attach a hoop to each end of the tube as shown and there is your paper plane.

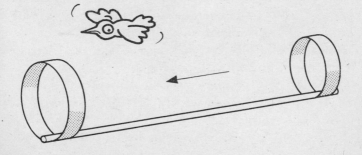

It is possible to make this sort of plane using a drinking straw for the body. You may have to experiment with hoop sizes and widths until you get a really good model.

To fly it hold it high with the larger hoop at the front and throw it like a dart, aiming slightly downwards. This plane doesn't do many aerobatics, but it is very good at gliding long distances and losing height slowly. If you and your friends make several models you could have distance-gliding competitions.

I hope that was plane enough for you. Now for some fun with plain paper.

How big is a hole?

Take a plain piece of paper. It can be any size but I recommend a sheet of A4 (297 × 210mm). The question now is how big a hole can you make in your piece of paper? Your first guess will probably be a hole slightly smaller than the paper itself. In fact, you can make a hole a whole lot bigger than that. Remember Doctor Who's *Tardis* with its inside much larger than the outside? The Doctor says that the *Tardis* has the ability to be in two places at once, and so he places the inside quite close so that it looks large, but the outside he places some distance away to make it look smaller. Well, that's the Doctor's explanation, but you'd need to be a Time Lord to really understand it. It's a sort of time-warp effect. Using a paper-warping effect, you can make a hole in your piece of paper big enough to go right round your room.

Fold your paper in half lengthways and then get

some scissors. Starting ½cm along the folded edge, make a cut upwards and stop ½cm from the top. Make similar cuts right along the folded edge at intervals of 1cm.

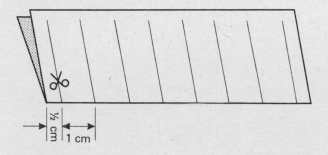

When you have done this, open out the paper and make horizontal cuts as indicated by the dotted lines on the diagram below. You will end up with a frame of paper with lots of paper fingers in it.

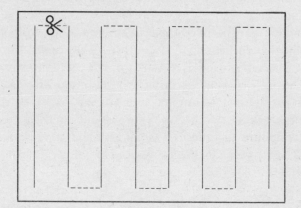

Now you need to cut from the outside edge right up the

middle of each finger, stopping ½cm from the end of the finger. These cuts are made alternately from each side.

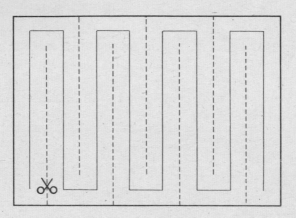

Our diagram shows that paper with its cuts still lying neat and flat. You will find that your piece flops all over the place.

If you have followed these instructions carefully you should have a zigzaggy paper strip that opens out to form a massive loop. Using A4 paper, the loop should measure about 12m all round. My daughter Zoe's room measures 3m × 3m and the loop just about goes round her four walls. With cuts closer together there is no knowing how big a loop it is possible to make. Perhaps the *Guinness Book of Records* would be interested in the result?

Getting in a twist

How many of you wear your hair in pigtails? OK, boys don't need to answer that question. I'm sure everyone knows that to form a pigtail you usually divide the hair into three bunches and 'plait' it by folding the bunches over each other.

Take a piece of paper and make two cuts in it to form three strips as shown.

Now ask someone if it is possible to plait the three strips even though they are joined at both ends. Most probably your friend will think it can't be done, and this is where you fool him.

Hold the strip under the table, or at least out of sight. Put your left hand through and *behind* the centre strip.

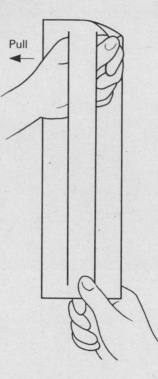

Take hold of the top of the strip and pull your hand out again. The right hand holds the bottom of the strip. Your strip should resemble the shape in the following diagram.

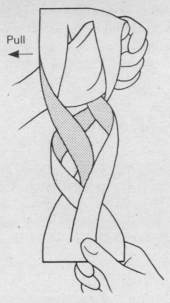

Pull

Put your left hand through and *in front* of the middle strip. Take hold of the top of the strip and pull it through again.

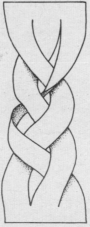

These two actions take about four seconds and you amaze your friend by revealing the beautifully plaited strip. Now you know how it's done you can give old trouser or skirt belts a new lease of life with fancy plaits.

The plaiting game

While we are on the subject of plaits, here is a pencil-and-paper game based on the plaiting principle. First draw three vertical lines and letter them A, B and C. (This game can be played with four or more lines, but I'll explain it using three.) At the bottom of one of the lines draw a box containing the letter 'T' for treasure.

Decide who should go first. The first player then secretly joins any two lines with a horizontal bar line. (He has the choice of joining A to B, A to C [disregard the B in the middle] or B to C.) He then covers the top of the paper, including his bar line, with another sheet of paper and passes it to the next player. She marks a secret bar line, lowers the covering paper to hide it and passes the paper back. The game continues until each player has had about five turns and then they each try to guess which letter is linked to the treasure. The path of each line is plotted down the page until the winner is found. Our diagram shows a typical game.

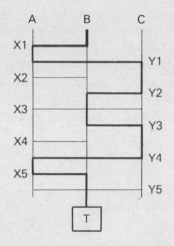

Player X first joined A to B, then player Y joined A to C. Then player X joined A to B again, and so on. At the end of the game, the result is traced by following the lines down until you come to a junction when you must cross to a new line. The line joining A to C does not affect B at all. In our example, B is the winner.

All-over pattern

If you have tiles on your bathroom walls they are
probably square. Square shapes cover flat surfaces very
neatly. A look at a brick wall will show you that oblong
or rectangular shapes will do the job just as well. Fancy
tiles can come in triangles or hexagons or diamond
shapes and sometimes they have curved sides.

The question is, how many four-sided or quadrilateral shapes are there that will cover a flat surface
perfectly? The answer is infinite millions.

Take a wodge of paper (old newspaper will do) a
good dozen or so sheets thick. Now take a pair of
scissors and cut out any four-sided shape you like. Here
are some examples:

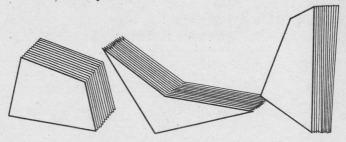

If you cut through all the sheets simultaneously, you
will have a dozen or so identical shapes. Now try to lay
them out on a table so that they fit together and leave no
gaps between them. You may have to experiment a bit
to work out how to do it, but it's really very easy. You
lay down one shape and then turn four shapes through
180 degrees and lay them alongside the first shape. You
can see that each side fits along an identical side, but

going the other way. Now fill four gaps with shapes the
original way round. Eventually you will have a pattern
of shapes facing alternate ways. It works every time!

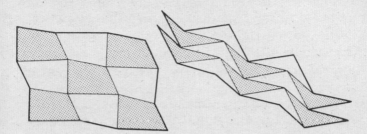

Curious curves

Take an oblong piece of paper and mark a dot a little
way from the centre point on one side.

Now fold the paper so that the edge just touches the spot and make a crease. Fold the paper again so that another point on the edge touches the spot. Make another crease. Continue to do this so that you have brought lots of points on the edge to the spot and have made lots of creases. Eventually you will find that the creases themselves form a shape. This shape is called a *parabola*, or to be more correct, a *parabolic curve*.

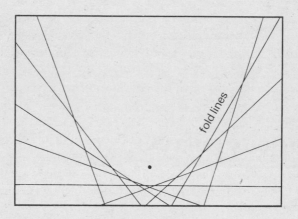

fold lines

So what good is a diabolic parabolic curve? Well, car headlights take the shape of parabolic curves. A light bulb placed where the dot is would reflect its light from the curve in parallel lines. Aerials that receive messages from satellites are shaped like this too. All the waves travelling in parallel lines hit the aerial and are bounced to the focal point (where the dot is) and this helps to amplify the signals received.

Many people find this curve very pleasing to the eye. The brain, in fact, is very good at understanding parabolic curves. Most of us can learn to catch a ball that is thrown to us because the ball's flight always takes the path of a parabolic curve which our brain learns to understand through experience.

Here is another curve you can produce. First, you need to draw a large circle and cut it out carefully. If you haven't got a pair of compasses handy, draw round a plate or a gramophone record. (The record is better because the hole in the middle will help you to find the centre of the circle.)

Next mark a dot somewhere inside the circle fairly close to the edge. Now fold the paper so that the edge touches the spot and makes a crease. Fold the paper again so that another point on the edge meets the spot and make another crease. Continue to make lots of creases by bringing lots of points on the edge of the circle in line with the spot. Eventually the creases will form themselves into a shape rather like an egg. This shape is called an *ellipse*.

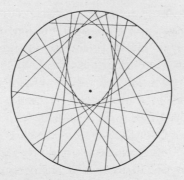

A much simpler way to make an ellipse is to pin some paper to a board. Stick two pins in the paper as shown below, then make a loop of string which fits round the two pins and leave a bit of slack. Take up the slack with a pencil and keeping the string tight, draw your ellipse.

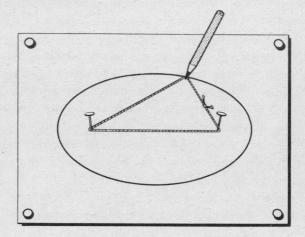

By drawing an ellipse in this way you can understand its properties. The ellipse has two foci (pronounced *foe-sigh*) which, in the folded version, coincide with the centre of your circle and the spot you marked near the edge. (The singular of foci is focus, but focus is pronounced *foe-cuss*, of cuss, I mean of course.)

Here is a problem. If you were a fly (you'd have to be a very clever one to be reading this) and you wanted to walk from one focus to the other via a point on the ellipse, which way would you walk to make sure of taking the shortest path? Well, it doesn't matter which direction you take because the distance from one focus to the other focus via any point on the ellipse is always the same. Just look at the string-drawn ellipse and you'll see it's true.

On a recent 'Think of a Number' programme we showed an ellipse-shaped billiard table. Apparently they were on sale some years ago in America but we had ours specially made for the programme. With one pocket situated at one focus point and a ball placed on the other focus, I asked a volunteer to find a way to pot the ball in the pocket going via the side cushion.

Once again, the direction doesn't matter. Wherever the ball hits the cushion it should bounce right into the pocket. Even if the cue passes over the pocket and hits the ball directly away from it, the ball should bounce from the cushion, cross the other focus, bounce off the cushion again and roll straight into the pocket.

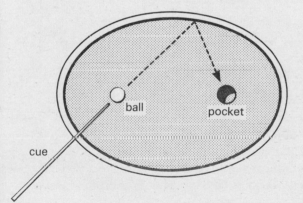

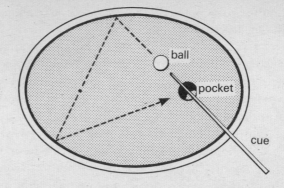

The ellipse is the path taken by planets as they spin round the sun, and it was the behaviour of planets in the elliptical orbits that helped Isaac Newton discover the laws of motion and the principles of universal gravitation.

Lewis Carroll's elliptical-wheeled cart

Besides being the author of *Alice in Wonderland*, Lewis Carroll was an accomplished mathematician and very fond of tricks and puzzles. In one of his books, a character points out how to achieve the feeling of sailing on choppy seas while riding in a horse-drawn cart. All you need to do is to fit the cart with elliptical wheels.

You need: cardboard
2 thin sticks *or*
2 pencils sharpened at both ends
thin string
scissors
2 pins

Using the two-pin-and-string method, make four elliptical wheels from stiff card.

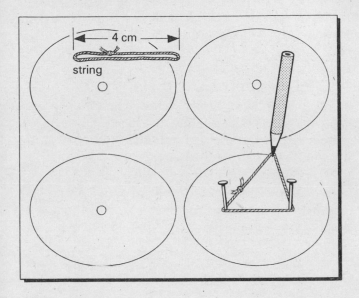

Make a hole in the centre of each wheel and push them onto the pencil axles. Round pencils are best. Attach them to the cart as shown, making sure you tie them loosely enough to turn. (A shoe-box lid works very well as the cart.)

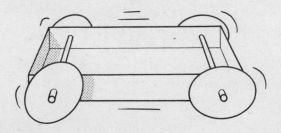

With the four wheels in identical positions you will notice that the cart rises and falls as it goes along. With the wheels at their highest point on one side and at their lowest on the other, the cart will rock from side to side. With the front wheels set on their highest points and the rear wheels set on their lowest, the cart will pitch forwards and backwards.

I will leave you with two problems. Can you set the wheels so that the cart rolls from side to side *and* pitches forward and back at the same time? And can you set the wheels so that the cart runs smoothly? (*Hint*: try setting the wheels a quarter-turn apart.)

CHAPTER 7

Nimble number tricks

Long ago magicians were called sorcerers, but not because they juggled with saucers. It was because they dabbled in sorcery or magic spells. Today magicians dabble in magic tricks, although they may also perform saucer-juggling or even jug-juggling in addition to their trick-trickery. It is more likely, however, that they spend much of their time juggling number tricks. Let me explain.

Sl(eight) of hand!

Magicians reach the top of their profession by presenting magical feats that appear absolutely unique but, more often than not, each brand new effect is achieved by disguising one of the old number tricks – tricks that are very simple and actually work themselves. Here are a few of the oldest and still most widely used, although you'd hardly ever spot them.

The brilliant bibliographical brain

A bit of forward planning is needed here. First select any book with more than 108 pages. A telephone directory is fine. Secretly look up page 108 and count down nine lines from the top left-hand corner. Now memorize the telephone number or, if you have chosen a novel, the first word on the ninth line. You're now ready to perform the trick.

First mention to your audience that you are a member of the BBB Society. It stands for Brilliant Bibliographical Brain. Then explain that you can only become a member if you can memorize a book completely from beginning to end. What you now propose to do is to get a volunteer to select just one number or word from the book that you have memorized, but to make it more interesting, you are going to do it by numbers.

Ask your helper to write down any three-figure number, all the figures being different – for example, 472. Now ask her to reverse the number and take the smaller number from the larger (472 − 274 = 198). (If the result should be a two-figure number, ask her to put a nought at the beginning.) Now ask her to reverse this number and add the two numbers together (981 + 198 = 1089). Point out that the result is a four-figure number chosen at random, is it not? She will tell you 'yes'. Ask for the first three figures and you have the page in the book. When she has found the page, ask her for the last figure and to count down that number of lines from the top left-hand corner. When she has reached the ninth line you tell her precisely the number or word she has arrived at. You can make it look difficult by concentrating hard before you come up with the answer.

To make things easier for your helper in this trick, all the calculations can be done on a pocket calculator. Ask her to punch in any three-figure number, all the figures being different. Now ask her to punch the minus sign and then the reverse of the number. The result should be a three-figure number. If it is a two-figure number ask her to imagine it has a nought at the beginning. If the number showing is a minus number, tell your helper to punch the minus sign and the reverse of the number. If the number is not minus, ask her to punch the plus sign and the reverse of the number. Point out that the result is a four-figure number chosen at random, is it not? Complete the trick as explained above.

In our example the answer was 1089, but that was no surprise because no matter what number you start with, if you follow the instructions, the answer is always 1089.

Pair-picking time

To 'prepair' for this pair-picking trick you need eight pieces of paper with a number on each side. The numbers should be:

22 / 37   16 / 31   18 / 33   38 / 53   20 / 35   36 / 51
24 / 39   26 / 41

These are your pairs of numbers. (This trick has nothing to do with the edible variety of pears.) Either give the eight pieces of paper to one person or one each to eight people and ask them to lay their paper on the table or hold it up so that just one side is showing. This is done while your back is turned. Explain that when they are ready you will turn round and add up the eight numbers showing almost instantaneously. How? Easy. It's a trick, isn't it? Let me explain.

First have a look at the pairs of numbers. Notice anything? The difference between each pair is always 15. Notice anything else? The lowest number in each pair is always *even*. If you add up the eight even numbers the total is exactly 200. That is all you need to know. When your helpers are ready you turn round and simply count the *odd* numbers showing. If, for example, there are four odd numbers showing, you remember the 200, add $4 \times 15 = 60$, and promptly shout out 260.

This is a trick that can be dressed up to look really impressive by adding more pairs of numbers and putting them on cards. After the cards have been shuffled and turned round, you can deal them out very quickly to give the answer.

The billion-pound brain

With this trick you can quickly grab the interest of the audience by pointing out that you have an uncle who works for the Treasury. Add that you cannot actually divulge what his job is, top secret and all that, but that he is so important he only deals in amounts of money that run into billions of pounds. In fact, to make his job easier, your uncle has devised a system of remembering numbers in the billion range, which takes some doing as a billion (1, 000,000,000) is a ten-figure number.

Now produce a pile of cards that you have 'prepaired' beforehand. Each card has a two-figure number on one side and a ten-figure number on the other. Here are a few examples:

$$25 / 7527965167$$
$$33 / 6730336954$$
$$57 / 4370774156$$
$$81 / 1909987527$$
$$87 / 1347189763$$

Ask someone to choose a card secretly and to tell you the two-figure number. Then, using your uncle's system, you will tell your helper the ten-figure number. This is how you do it.

To arrive at the ten-figure number you simply take the two-figure number away from 100. Thus, in the first example, $100 - 25 = 75$. You call out 7 . . . 5 . . . Then add the two digits in the answer together $(7 + 5 = 12)$. Forget the 10 and just call out 2. That's 7 . . . 5 . . . 2 . . . Add the last two digits $(5 + 2 = 7)$ and call out 7. That's 7 . . . 5 . . . 2 . . . 7 . . . Continue to add the last two figures, ignoring tens wherever they arise. This sounds complicated but with a little practice it becomes easy. Try it and see.

The only problem with this trick is knowing when you have shouted out exactly ten digits. The best way to do this is to place your hands on your head (just as your uncle does because it helps him to concentrate) and tap your fingers one at a time as you call out each digit.

A professional magician might dress up this trick further by substituting objects for the two-figure numbers. You could show a Christmas pudding to represent 25 (remember that December 25 is Christmas Day), a pair of legs for 11 and a can of beans for 57 (Heinz). I'm sure you'll be able to think of lots more. If you do this trick well you're bound to impress everyone who sees it, even your uncle who works for the Treasury!

The magical matrix

Matrix might be a new word to you but it's not difficult to remember. It's simply a network of numbered squares. The layout for a game of noughts and crosses is a three-by-three matrix, as there are three squares on each side. The matrix trick I'm going to show you can be down with a matrix of any size you like, but I'm going to explain it using a four-by-four matrix.

7	15	14	8
5	13	12	6
3	11	10	4
6	14	13	7

Find four titchy pieces of paper and place one piece on any square you like. Now place the second piece of paper on any other square as long as it is not in the same horizontal row or vertical column as the first piece. Next place the third piece on another square that is not in the same row or column as either of the first two. You now have one piece left and you will find just one square that is not in the same row or column as the other three. Place the fourth piece of paper in that square. Then carefully add up the numbers covered with the pieces of paper. OK? I predict that your answer will be 37. Amazing!

This is how it works. Here is the same square again with some other figures round it:

	1	9	8	2
6	7	15	14	8
4	5	13	12	6
2	3	11	10	4
5	6	14	13	7

From this you should be able to work out how the numbers in the squares were determined. The 7 in the top left-hand corner is the sum of 6 + 1. Next to it number 15 is the sum of 6 + 9 and so on. If you add up the numbers printed round the sides, the total is 37. In doing the trick, I made you choose four numbers in such a way that you chose one in each row and one square in each column so that the numbers round the side feature in the answer once and once only. Therefore, the answer had to be 37.

A good magician would be able to form a square which would give any selected number as a result. You could do the same with a little bit of practice. The square above shows how easily it can be done. The numbers across the top are easy to remember (1982 is this year) and these numbers add up to 20. Down the side, 6 + 4 = 10 and 2 + 5 = 7. For a square with a result of 35 you would simply change the last 5 to a 3, and adjust the bottom row accordingly.

This trick is ideal for a personalized birthday card. If you have a friend who is fourteen soon, draw up a square like the one below and work the trick for that person on his birthday.

	0	3	1	2
1	1	4	2	3
4	4	7	5	6
3	3	6	4	5
0	0	3	1	2

A *diabolical magic square*

Magic squares have fascinated people for centuries. The most widely known, which dates back at least 2000 years, is a three-by-three magic square. To form this square write the first nine digits as shown, then swap the corner numbers over and squash the square into a diamond shape.

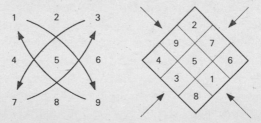

Now you have a magic square in which the numbers in each row and each column always add up to 15. However, the magic square shown below is much more complex and it is so fascinating that it has become known as the diabolical magic square.

14	1	12	7
11	8	13	2
5	10	3	16
4	15	6	9

In this square each row and column adds up to 34 and you can use this basic square to form a magic square with a constant chosen by anyone at random.

Ask someone to suggest any number between 34 and 50. Let's assume he says 43. If you have remembered the square shown above all you have to do is draw a four-by-four matrix and start to fill in the numbers. (It looks more effective if you fill them in in random order.) While doing this, and to make the trick work, you need to adjust the numbers in the four shaded squares as follows. Take 34 from the selected number (43) and you get 9. To each of the four shaded squares you must add 9 and enter the new number to give you the square shown on the next page.

23	1	12	7
11	8	22	2
5	10	3	25
4	24	6	9

Your helper will be impressed when he finds that the columns and rows all add up to 43, but don't stop there. Point out that the reason this square is called diabolical is that the magical number 43 can be arrived at in 36 different ways.

The four rows add up to 43.

The four columns add up to 43.

The two diagonals add up to 43.

The six broken diagonals make 43 (e.g. 11 + 1 + 6 + 25).

The nine different groups of four squares make 43 (e.g. 1 + 12 + 8 + 22).

The six groups of opposite pairs in each 8 × 2 oblong make 43 (e.g. 5 + 4 + 25 + 9).

The four corners make 43 (23 + 7 + 4 + 9).

The corners of each of four 3 × 3 squares make 43 (e.g. 23 + 12 + 5 + 3).

Diabolically clever, isn't it?

CHAPTER 8

Timely tricks
and date-divining

A philosopher once said, 'Any man who has a watch knows the time, but a man who has two watches is never certain.' This is absolutely true, because no two watches keep exactly the same time. In 1964 scientists in Washington, DC, produced the most accurate time-keeping device ever constructed, but to ensure its accuracy they made two devices so that one could keep a check on the other and the average time could be taken. These clocks are accurate to within one second in 1,700,000 years, which is more accurate than the Earth itself. But you can't have something more accurate than the Earth to measure hours and days, so it's all very confusing.

Lewis Carroll pointed out how silly time-keeping is when he said that rather than have a watch that lost a minute a day, it was better to have a watch that didn't go at all. At least a stopped watch is right twice every day, but a watch that loses a minute a day is only right once every 720 days which is about two years. Today many people have watches which only lose one second a day, but they are in real trouble, because their watches will only tell the correct time once every 120 years.

Time-tapping

I own one of those digital watches. (If I want to know the time, I have to press a little button with my digit.) Recently I have noticed that analogue watches (those with the twelve numbers on a round face) are coming back into fashion. Here is a trick which you can perform with one of those watches. It involves tapping on the face of the watch or clock, which is all right if you use a pencil or your finger, but not so good if you use a cricket bat or hammer.

First ask someone to select any number on the dial without telling you, and to remember that number. Now explain that you are going to start tapping the numbers on the watch, and you want your helper to count the taps in her head, starting with the number she has chosen. So, if she thought of the number 'four', on the first tap she must count 'four' in her head, 'five' on the next tap, and so on until she reaches twenty, when she must shout 'stop'. When she shouts stop, you will be pointing to the chosen number.

This is how it works. For the first eight taps you can tap any number on the watch, counting with each tap, in your head. Your ninth tap must be on the number twelve and the next tap on the number eleven and so on, tapping backwards round the face. You won't know when your helper gets to twenty until she shouts stop, but when that happens, as if by magic, you will be pointing at the number she had secretly chosen.

Guess your age

When you are young you tend to know the ages of all your friends because you know which class they are in at school. Also, people change so quickly when they are growing up that you can usually tell the difference between someone who is eleven and someone who is thirteen quite easily. However, with adults age becomes a bit of a niggly point and many of them go to great lengths to keep their ages a secret. Not me though, I don't mind anyone knowing that I am twenty-one and a bit (although it's quite a big bit!). This trick will help you to get the true age out of anyone before they know what's happening.

Ask someone to think of his age and add 92.

Example: Age   34
                 + 92
                 ───────
                    126

Then say, 'The number you now have is in the hundreds, isn't it? It's not in the two hundreds, is it?' He will tell you that it is in the hundreds. Now ask him to take the 1 from the beginning of the number and add it to the remaining two-figure number.

                    26
                 +   1
                 ───────
                    27

You now point out that he has a number which bears no relation to his real age. He will agree with this and so you ask him for the number. When he reveals it, you simply add on 7 to get his age. From our example you can see that in the middle of the sum you took 99 away, and the two numbers added at the beginning and the end also add up to 99, bringing you back to the actual age. Simple, isn't it?

Here is another guess-your-age trick which is a little more complicated but well worth trying because the effect is staggering. It works well with a pocket calculator. First ask someone to take the pocket calculator and punch in any number she likes. The number can have three or four or even six digits; it doesn't matter as long as it doesn't overload the calculator. Now ask her to press the minus key and feed in the reverse of the number. Then ask her whether the result is an ordinary number or a minus number. If it is ordinary, ask her to add her age to it. If it is a minus number, ask her to subtract her age. Now ask her to add up all the digits in the result and to tell you the answer. With just a few seconds' delay you then tell her exactly how old she is. How?? Well, have a look at this example for someone who is forty-one years old:

Choose any number: 75689
Minus the reverse: −98657
                     ─────────
                     −22968

(The digits in the answer always add up to nine:
 $2 + 2 + 9 + 6 + 8 = 27; 2 + 7 = 9$.)

The number is a minus, so take away your age:
                     −22968
                   −   41
                   ─────────
                   −23009

Add the digits: $2 + 3 + 0 + 0 + 9 = 14; 1 + 4 = 5$.

This process of adding the digits in a number is called finding the digital root. You now know that the digital root of your helper's age is five. To find all the ages with a digital root of five, you keep adding nines to five and you get 5, 14, 23, 32, 41, 50, 59, 68, 77, 86, 95 and so on. Notice how in each number the digits eventually add up to five (9 + 5 = 14; 1 + 4 = 5). Now I'm sure that just by looking at a person you can tell his or her age to within ten years. So in your head you say, 'She's not 5, add 9, or 14, add 9, or 23, add 9, or 32, add 9, so she must be 41.' This is such a good trick, because the actual working seems to have nothing whatsoever to do with the person's age.

An extraordinary coincidence

Popular Sunday newspapers often carry stories of incredible coincidences, like people finding lost relatives after years of separation or precious objects that were lost ages ago turning up quite unexpectedly. I once heard the story of a girl who got married and went to the Isle of Wight for her honeymoon. Unfortunately, while crossing the Solent on the ferry, her new wedding ring fell overboard into the water. Exactly twenty-five years later she and her husband paid a return visit to the Isle of Wight and on the first evening in the hotel restaurant she ordered Dover sole. The fish was served and when she cut it open, guess what she found inside? Bones of course! The hand of coincidence doesn't stretch that far – or does it? Now can you explain the extraordinary coincidence in the following comparison between the lives of Margaret Thatcher and Ronald Reagan?

Margaret Thatcher

Born	1925
Main career milestone: Leader of Conservative Party	1975
Age this year	57
Years since taking over leadership	7
Total:	3964

Ronald Reagan

Born	1911
Main career milestone: Governor of California	1967
Age this year	71
Years since taking over governorship	15
Total:	3964

Amazing, isn't it? I'll explain all at the end of this chapter.

The maddening months

Here is a silly question. How many months have thirty days? The answer is all of them except February, but when it comes to remembering which of them have thirty-one days, it's a bit confusing. When I was at school we were taught a rhyme to help us remember, but we adapted that to read, 'Thirty days hath September, April, June and November. All the rest have thirty-one – and it's not bloomin' fair!'

Just in case you can't remember the rhyme, here is another way of always knowing how many days each month contains. Clench your fists and hold them up side by side with the backs of your hands facing you. Now imagine the knuckles and the gaps in between are each given a month, as in the diagram below. Now it's easy to remember that counting from the left, each knuckle represents a month with thirty-one days and each gap between the knuckles represents a month with thirty days, except of course for the first gap which represents February, which has only twenty-eight days or twenty-nine in a leap year.

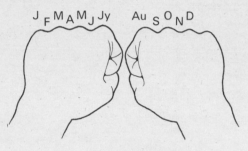

Do you remember the day you were born?

I wonder how many of you remember the day you were born. I know my memory doesn't seem to go back that far. My mum remembers that event very well and she says she remembers that it was a Monday, but I'm sure she was too busy that day to be looking at calendars. However, if you would like to know the day on which you were born, or indeed the actual day on which any date fell, then this trick is for you.

You need to make three separate calculations for this

trick, so until you are used to it, it's best to work with a pencil and paper. For our example, let's work out which day 31 May 1950 fell on.

The year This method works for any date in the twentieth century.

First take the last two figures
of the year: 50

Now divide by 4 and forget any
remainder (50 ÷ 4 = 12½): 12

Add the two numbers and remember
the answer: 62

This is the only difficult bit. You have to remember a table which goes as follows:

January	1
February	4
March	4
April	0
May	2
June	5
July	0
August	3
September	6
October	1
November	4
December	6

This is easier to remember if you group the numbers like this:

144
025
036
146

These numbers can be remembered like this:

12 squared
5 squared
6 squared
12 squared + 2

If you can't remember, then you need to keep this table somewhere handy so that you can check with it. In our example, May has the number 2, so we add 2 to our total:

$$62$$
$$+ \; 2$$
$$\overline{64}$$

The day Simply add the day of the month:

$$+31$$
$$\overline{\cdot \; 95}$$

There is just one point to watch. If the date you are looking for falls in January or February of a leap year, then you must subtract one, otherwise you're nearly there. Divide the total by 7 and note the remainder because it's only the remainder you're looking for.

$$95 \div 7 = 13 \text{ with the remainder } 4$$

This table helps you find the day:

Sunday	Monday	Tuesday	Wednesday	Thursday	Friday	Saturday
1	2	3	4	5	6	0

Now simply count 4 from Sunday which gives you the answer Wednesday. (If the remainder had been nought, the day would have been Saturday.) So now you can declare that 31 May 1950 fell on a Wednesday. This method is really very simple if you practise, and once you perform it for one person you'll be surprised how everyone else gathers round asking you to do it. But here is a warning. I think you had better buy or borrow a calendar because once you've performed this trick on a friend, you really have no excuse for forgetting his or her birthday. Besides, you'll need a calendar to perform the next two tricks.

The one-day-per-week trick

To begin this trick, flip through a calendar until you find a month with five Wednesdays. There are only about four of these months in each year as they can only occur when Wednesday falls on the 1st, 2nd or 3rd of the month. To perform this trick you need to know the total of the dates on which the five Wednesdays fall. This is quite easy to remember if Wednesday falls on the 1st; the total is 75. With Wednesday falling on the 2nd, the total is 80 and with Wednesday falling on the 3rd, the total is 85. In our example Wednesday falls on the 1st and so the total is 75 and this is your *guide* number. Once you know this number you can perform the trick blindfolded, or at least with your back to the calendar.

Ask someone to note that there are five rows of dates in the month, either five weeks or parts of weeks. Ask her to mark off five dates, one in each row or week, after which you will rapidly reveal the total of those five dates. When she has chosen the five dates, ask her how many of each day she has chosen as follows. How many Sundays? How many Mondays? How many Tuesdays?

And so on. For each answer you must adjust your guide number according to the following table:

Sunday	Monday	Tuesday	Wednesday	Thursday	Friday	Saturday
−3	−2	−1	0	+1	+2	+3

It is easiest to perform the calculation in two parts. In our example the first answers would be one Sunday, one Monday, no Tuesdays. You could stop your helper at this point and calculate in your head:

$$75 - 3 \text{ (Sun.)} - 2 \text{ (Mon.)} = 70$$

Ask her to continue. You would, of course, ignore any Wednesdays and listen to her replies: 'Two Thursdays, no Fridays and one Saturday.' From these answers you would calculate:

$$70 + 2 (2 \times 1 \text{ [Thurs.]} + 3 \text{ (Sat.)} = 75$$

Thus, you would give 75 as your answer. On adding the five dates she should find that you are absolutely correct.

The Nine-Day Wonder

If you examine the numbers on a calendar, you may soon notice how easy it is to perform tricks with them because of the way the numbers are arranged. For instance, given the number 15 you always know that the number above it must be 15 − 7 which is 8 and the number below it must be 15 + 7 which is 22. In fact, if you ask someone to choose three numbers in a line vertically, horizontally or diagonally and then to tell you the centre number, you can always tell the total of the three numbers by multiplying by 3. For example, if the number given is nine, the total of the three numbers must always be 9 × 3 which is 27.

		1	2	3	4	5
6	7	8	9	10	11	12
13	14	15	16	17	18	19
20	21	22	23	24	25	26
27	28	29	30	31		

Using this principle you can perform a very impressive trick which I call the Nine-Day Wonder. While you turn your back, ask someone to choose any month on the calendar and from that month choose nine days that form a square of three rows of three dates per row. Ask him to draw a line round his selected nine days. Make sure that he has understood the instructions and just by the way ask him for the smallest number in the square. In our example diagram, the number is 5 and that's all you need to know.

				1	2	3
4	5	6	7	8	9	10
11	12	13	14	15	16	17
18	19	20	21	22	23	24
25	26	27	28	29	30	31

Now explain that you really only want three numbers from the square, so ask him to select any number in the

square and to draw a ring round it. When he has done
that ask him to cross out the numbers in the square that
are in the same row as the circled number and also to
cross out those in the same column above or below the
circled number. Then ask him to select another number
which has not been touched and to put a ring round
that. Once again he is then to cross out all numbers in
the same row and all numbers in the same column as
this number. Lastly, tell him he will find one number
which is still unmarked and ask him to put a ring round
that number. Immediately this is done, point out that if
he adds the three circled numbers, the answer will be
39.

				1	2	3
4	X	⑥	X	8	9	10
11	X	X	⑭	15	16	17
18	⑲	X	X	22	23	24
25	26	27	28	29	30	31

How is it done? Well, when he tells you the smallest
number in the square, all you need to do is to add 8 and
this will give you the centre number in the square.
Multiply that number by 3 and you have the answer no
matter which three numbers he chose to put rings
round. That's how to do the wonderful Nine-Day
Wonder trick and it should leave your audience
wondering for a little while.

The Maggie and Ronnie coincidence explained

The coincidence in the career dates of Prime Minister Margaret Thatcher and President Ronald Reagan seems at first to be quite amazing, but really it's a prime example of the way numerologists can manipulate numbers so that the numbers themselves seem to be conveying a message.

To explain the coincidence you only need to divide 3964 by 2. This gives you 1982 which happens to be this year (at the time of writing) and the year in which the calculations were made. If Margaret Thatcher was born in 1925 she must be 57 this year, and the two figures added must give us the answer 1982. The same goes for the other calculations we have used. Using this trick, you can demonstrate a link between any number of people, and until you explain the trick, you'll be delighted with the number of people who are taken in by these 'amazing coincidences'.

CHAPTER 9

Tricks with odds and ends

When a magician on television opens some curtains to reveal an enormous packing case and an Indian elephant, you automatically know that he is going to use trick curtains or a trick packing case, or even a trick elephant to achieve his effect. If you are clever and spot how the trick is done, it won't do you much good because you haven't got a trick set of curtains or packing case and you probably don't even have an elephant around the house. (Don't bother getting one – it'll cost you all your pocket money to keep it in buns.) It's probably best to leave this kind of trick to the experts because there are lots of very effective tricks that you can perform using everyday odds and ends that you'll find round the house. For instance, with a scarf and any piece of paper you can perform . . .

The single selection of a supersensory signal

This trick can be performed without any preparation and is especially effective at parties where quite a few people are gathered. The only props you need are a scarf and a sheet of paper, any kind at all. Ask someone to blindfold you with the scarf and for further security you can be turned to face the wall. You then ask the members of your audience to raise their hands if they would like to convey a special number to you. It could be a car number, a telephone number, a birthday or a special date – any number at all. Ask them not to call out. Ask the person who blindfolded you to select just one person with a hand raised. While the selection is being made, you tear the sheet of paper into pieces. Then ask your helper to pass a piece of paper to the selected person who must then write the number he wishes to convey on the paper. Ask your helper to pass out the remaining pieces of paper to other people in the audience, instructing them to write any number they wish on the paper. When this is done the helper collects the papers and she may mix them into any order she thinks fit. Now the blindfold is removed and you ask everyone to concentrate on the numbers they wrote down. You explain that your supersensory mind can detect signals coming from the special person who selected the first number. After carefully examining the papers and appearing to concentrate deeply, you read out the number that the first person wrote. Everyone is totally amazed and dumbfounded, but how is it done? The secret lies in the tearing of the paper.

While you are blindfolded, tear the paper into three pieces, making sure that the two outer pieces are placed on top of the middle piece. Square up the paper.

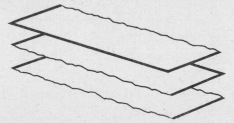

Next, turn the paper sideways and tear it into three again, placing the outer pieces on top of the centre pieces.

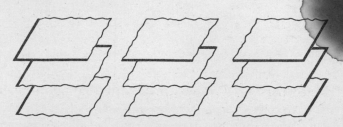

You now have nine pieces of paper and it is the bottom piece that you pass to the selected person. When you get the pieces back you will always be able to recognize that piece because it will be the only one with *four* torn edges.

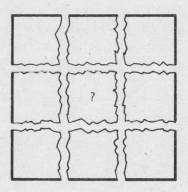

As an alternative you can perform the trick with a piece of paper torn from a larger sheet. In this case the unique piece of paper is the corner piece which will have two edges that are untorn.

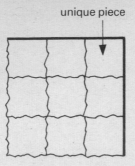

unique piece

Either way you do it, the trick usually fools everyone and yet it's really a bit of a rip-off!

The curious course of a curve

Here is a trick you can do when you're doodling with a pencil and paper. Draw a curving line that crosses itself five or six times and finally joins up with its beginning to make an endless loop, something like the one in the diagram.

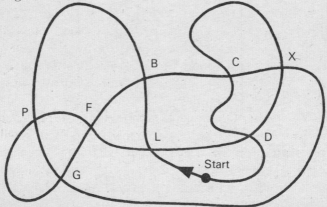

Now ask someone to draw a similar shape for himself in secret so that you don't see it. Next ask him to find each point where the line crosses itself and to give each point a different letter. Tell him to pick the letters at random and not in alphabetical order. When he has done that, ask him to choose any point on the curve as a starting point, as long as it isn't a junction. You must give the next instruction very carefully so that he understands exactly what he has to do. Ask him to trace a path right round the curve until it comes back to the starting point. Each time he comes to a junction he must shout out the letter at that junction. To make things more difficult, ask him to reverse the order of two of the letters. For example, he may be approaching the letter B with the letter F next in line, but he would call out FB instead of BF. He is to do this once and once only and he must be sure to call out all the other letters in their correct order as he comes to them. At the end of the complete circuit you will be able to tell him which two letters he switched. How you do this is simplicity itself.

You need a pencil and a piece of paper with a line drawn across it. As the letters are called out you write them down alternately above and below the line. In tracing the path round the loop, each letter will be called exactly twice, but if you examine your list when the path has been completed, you will see that each letter appears once above and once below the line *except* for the two letters that were switched. These letters will appear twice on the same side of the line.

L	P	X	F	G	F	D	C
B	G	C	B	P	L	X	D

In our example you can see that F and B must have been the letters that were switched. It's easy when you know how, but working out how it's done should drive your friends round the bend!

A rather crooked rope trick

Around a hundred years ago visitors to India would often return to Great Britain with amazing tales of the magical feats of mystics and street magicians who performed in bazaars and market places all over India and the Middle East. These tricks included fire-walking and snake-charming, but the most famous of all was the Indian rope trick.

Apparently the magician would throw a rope into the air where it would hang vertically with the bottom end just touching the floor, but with no visible means of support. Then a small boy would climb the rope and as he reached the top he would disappear into thin air. Although hundreds of people profess to have seen the trick performed, to this day no one has ever explained exactly how it is done.

However, if you can find a piece of rope and a friend (who needn't be too small) I will show you a trick that has absolutely nothing whatsoever to do with the Indian rope trick. I know it's a bit of a swizz, but so is the trick that I'm going to show you. In fact, I hope that the friend you choose to try it on is a good friend because you are going to cheat him or her something rotten. You see, this is one of those tricks that was used at country fairs to cheat people out of their money. First of all you have to gain your friend's confidence by giving her a game in which she has a fair chance of winning, rather like this:

The set-up

Take a length of rope (1m will be more than enough) or you can use a belt or a tie or even a string of beads. (My dad told me always to pick girlfriends who wore beads. He used to say, 'You can always count on a girl who wears beads.' My dad was mathematically minded too.)

Lay your rope out on a table or any flat surface as shown below.

Notice that we have marked the ends of the rope X and Y and the loop in the middle L. Pull X so that it lies across the middle of the curve and at the same time open out the loop with your fingers. In this way you form a curve with two distinct areas looking rather like a figure 8.

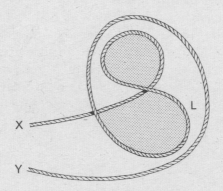

Ask your friend to place her finger in one of the two spaces in the figure 8. Explain that you will try to pull the rope away but she must try to get her finger caught in the loop. A bit of trial and error will show you that a finger placed in the lower space will be trapped, but a finger in the upper space will be left when the string is pulled away. (With a finger in both spaces, they are both caught.)

Give your friend a few tries and she will soon realize that to get her finger caught and win the game she must always choose the lower space. It is now, when she is confident of winning, that you perform the trick.

The trick

Lay out the rope as shown in the diagram on page 109, but this time as you shorten the X end, you turn the loop over before you spread out the rope to form the figure 8.

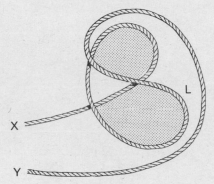

Watch your friend's face as she chooses the lower space but the string pulls away. Next she will try the upper loop, but once again the string will pull free. By setting up the diagram opposite, or the one above, you are in complete control of whether the trick works or not. Sneaky, isn't it?

Jumping elastic bands

The very first job I had when I left school was in an aircraft factory where there seemed to be an endless supply of pencils, paper clips and elastic bands. At first I thought the elastic bands were used to power the aircraft until I realized that the whole factory had been built to produce aircraft engines and propellers which were designed to do the job properly. My part in the production was to work out how much everything cost, and although I worked quite hard, I always seemed to have time to work out tricks to perform with odds and ends round the office.

My favourite piece of equipment was the elastic band, which came in handy for practical jokes like wrapping black bands round a black office telephone and then ringing the number from another phone in the office. Someone would grab the receiver but the rest of the phone would come with it!

Elastic bands can be used to propel all kinds of missiles, but the finest degree of accuracy proved to be in using the elastic band itself as the missile. If you hook a band over the end of the first finger and thumb, all you have to do is bend the thumb slightly and the elastic band flies forward.

With practice my colleagues and I could hit flies at several yards and also score a hole in one in a coffee cup some ten feet away. At that distance we could also spin round, as in a western gunfight, and hit the hand of someone firing at us.

Of course, these antics aren't the sort of things that you can put in a book of tricks and puzzles, so here is the only trick I ever learnt with an elastic band. The idea is to put an elastic band over the first and second fingers of one hand and make it jump magically to the third and fourth fingers. All you need to do is place the elastic band over the first two fingers and then close your hand into a loose fist. As you do this, you thread all four finger ends into the elastic band.

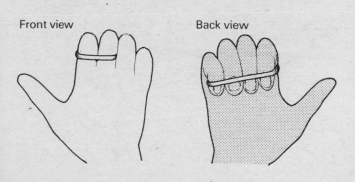

Front view   Back view

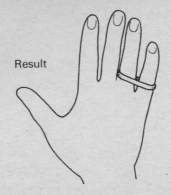

Result

You're now ready to astound some innocent member of the public. Show your hand with the elastic band over the first two fingers. Straighten out your fingers and, hey presto, the elastic band jumps to the third and fourth fingers. Thread your fingers back in again and the band will jump back again when you straighten out your hand.

To make this trick really impressive, take a second elastic band and thread it in and out of all four fingers, effectively locking the first band on to two fingers.

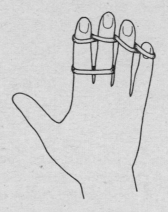

Now surely, the trick is impossible? Try it and see. Even you will be amazed when you see that the band can still jump from one pair of fingers to the other. It's finger-jumping good!

Paper clip linking

The only practical joke I ever played with paper clips was to link up a whole box of them into one long chain. When the chap next to me reached for one clip, the whole lot came out. The result wasn't worth the effort. However, there is an amazingly clever way of linking two paper clips without actually being in contact with them as they link up. For this you will need a pound note. (Any piece of strongish paper will do, but traditionally a pound note is used.)

First bend the note into an S shape and then attach the two paper clips as shown.

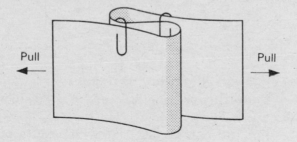

The two clips are not in contact with each other, but if you pull the ends of the pound note as if to straighten it out, the clips fly off the note and as they land everyone can see that, quite astonishingly, they have become linked up. It doesn't matter how many times I try this trick, the result always amazes me.

Tricks with dice

No one really knows how long dice have been among the odds and ends found in people's houses. Astragals, which are the ankle bones from cloven-hooved animals like sheep, were used as dice many thousands of years ago, but the oldest known manufactured dice, which are pyramid shaped, are at least 5000 years old. Astragals and pyramids have four sides, but today we are used to the six-sided variety which go back some 3000 years. So you see dice tricks must have been around for a long time. Here is one of the oldest tricks known.

Give someone three dice then, turn your back. Ask him to throw the dice and add up the spots showing on the upper faces. Now ask him to select any two of the dice and add to the total of the spots on the bottom faces. Ask him to throw the two dice again and add the two new upper faces. Then ask him to select any one of the three dice and add the bottom face of that die.

Now ask him to throw the die again and add the new upper face. On turning round you simply glance at the three dice and give the total your helper has arrived at. How is it done? Simple.

You must remember that normally dice have their spots arranged so that opposite faces add up to 7. The procedure you have made your helper perform seems quite complicated and it appears that you have no way of knowing what numbers were on the dice that were re-thrown. However, by adding in the bottom faces you know that each re-thrown dice added 7 to the total. There were three re-thrown dice so you simply add 21 to the spots showing on the three dice at the end of the trick and there is the total you were looking for. The trick is incredibly easy, but the procedure is complicated enough to confuse people and leave them wondering how you did it.

Think of a number with dice

Here is a dice trick along the lines of the usual 'Think of a number' trick. However, the use of a die or even three dice gives the trick a little more appeal. You can get your helper to write the calculations down as you go along if you think she may forget the calculations in the middle of the trick. Here is the procedure with example numbers to explain the working.

Roll a die. Take the uppermost number, double it and add 5:

$$4 \times 2 = 8 + 5 = 13$$

Multiply by 5: $13 \times 5 = 65$

Roll the second
die and add top
face: $65 + 2 = 67$

Multiply by 10 and
add 3: $67 \times 10 = 670 + 3 = 673$

Roll the third die
and add top face: $673 + 5 = 678$

You then ask for the total and instantly give the faces of the three dice thrown. This is done by simply subtracting the magic number 253: $678 - 253 = 425$ (4, 2 and 5).

If three dice are used they can now be revealed to prove you were right. Come to think of it you could perform the trick by asking your helper to think of three numbers and do without the dice, but then it wouldn't be a dice trick, would it? I'm touching on dicey ground here so let's have a really complex dice trick.

A mammoth dice trick

For this trick you need to make five special dice. This seems like a lot of trouble for a trick, but the effect is quite startling so why not have a go? The dice need to be six-sided so you can use building blocks or paper-covered Oxo cube boxes, but perhaps an easier way is to find five pencils or ball point pens that have six sides. Stick a strip of paper round the barrel of each pen or pencil and you are all set.

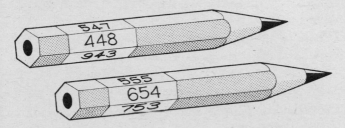

Number your dice in the following ways:

Die A	943	844	745	646	547	448
Die B	555	654	753	852	951	159
Die C	861	762	663	564	366	465
Die D	771	177	672	573	474	276
Die E	483	384	582	285	681	186

When you have numbered them your dice will look incredibly complicated, and yet, when you perform the trick you will be able to add up the five upper faces in an instant – but how? Well, let's examine the numbers on the dice. First look at the first and third digits in the numbers. On each die these digits always add up to the same total.

Die A	12
Die B	10
Die C	9
Die D	8
Die E	7

From this information you know that the total of the first and third digits on all five dice always add up to 46 (12 + 10 + 9 + 8 + 7 = 46).

Now look at the second digit in each number. The second digit on each die is always the same so the total of the five second digits will always be 30 (4 + 5 + 6 + 7 + 8 = 30). With this knowledge you can now add the upper faces very quickly like this.

Let's assume that you have rolled the five dice and each one is showing the first number in the list above, namely:

$$943$$
$$555$$
$$861$$
$$771$$
$$483$$

To find the total of all these numbers all you need to do is add up the five last digits: 3 + 5 + 1 + 1 + 3 = 13. This number forms the last two digits in the answer. You already know the middle digits add up to 30 so this won't affect the last two digits in the answer, but you need to add 3 to the first digit total. You know that the first and third digits add up to 46 so the first digits must add up to 46 − 13 = 33 + 3 (carried from middle column) = 36. So the total of all five numbers is 3613.

That's how the trick works, but you can make the method of calculating easier by simplifying the last sum. 46 − (something) + 3 is the same as 49 − (something), so all you need to do is add the last digits and take the total from 49. In our example, 49 − 13 = 36 and so 3613 is the answer.

It may sound complicated at first, but try it a few times and you'll be amazed at how simple it all is and how effective it is when you perform it.

CHAPTER 10

Solid, man, solid

Here is a problem involving some matches. Using five matches you can form a diamond shape made up of two equilateral triangles. (Equilateral means the sides are all the same length, so don't use broken matches!)

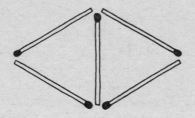

Now the problem is, given one more match, can you make four equilateral triangles without breaking any matches? The answer is simple when you know how. Four triangles can be formed by making a triangular pyramid shape as shown below.

This shape is called a tetrahedron because it has four faces. It is also one of the five *platonic solids*. The others are the cube or hexahedron, the octahedron, the dodecahedron and the icosahedron.

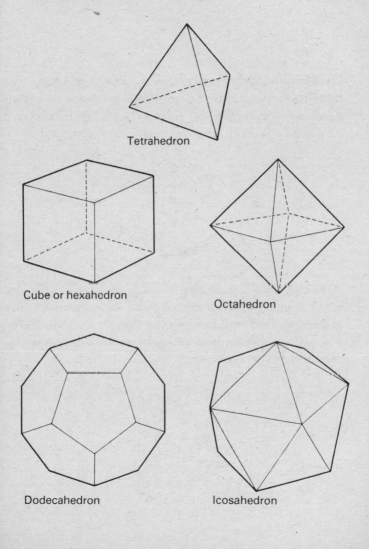

Tetrahedron

Cube or hexahedron

Octahedron

Dodecahedron

Icosahedron

They are called the five platonic solids because they are the only solids that can be made up of identical regular polygons. Each one has several interesting aspects to it.

The tetrahedron

The tetrahedron was the shape of the first known manufactured dice. You can make one from one large triangle divided into four small triangles as shown below.

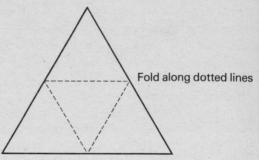

Fold along dotted lines

You may find this a bit tricky so I'll give you an easy method. Get an old oblong envelope and seal it. Fold the envelope in half lengthways.

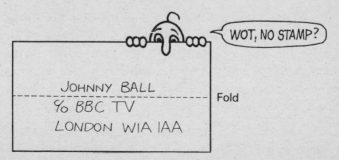

WOT, NO STAMP?

JOHNNY BALL
% BBC TV
LONDON WIA IAA

Fold

Now fold the right-hand edge of the envelope over so that the bottom right-hand corner reaches the centre fold. Make a pencil mark at this point.

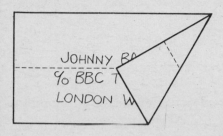

Next, accurately mark a line across the envelope passing through the mark and cut the envelope in two along that line.

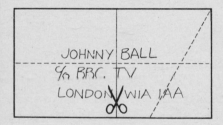

You only need the right end of the envelope, but if you have used a foolscap envelope you will have enough on the left-hand side to make another tetrahedron. With the right-hand end you need to make two folds running from the mark back to each of the original corners. These folds should be creased both ways.

Fold along dotted lines

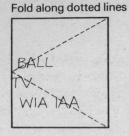

Now you can put your fingers inside the envelope and open it out to form the tetrahedron. Close the mouth of the envelope and seal it with sticky tape.

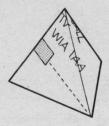

Wasn't that easy? If you make five of them you can group them together to form a fascinating five-edged wheel, and with twenty of them you can make an icosahedron, but that comes later.

The cube

The cube is sometimes called a hexahedron because it has six faces. It is the most common of all the platonic solids, probably because of the ease with which cubes pack together and can be piled up without falling over. As a cube has six square faces it can be made up from six connected squares drawn on a piece of paper, but not if the squares form a straight strip. There are actually eleven different ways of forming a grid of six squares that will fold to make a cube. One of them is the cross shape shown below.

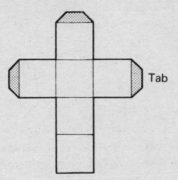

Tab

Can you work out the other ten? Have a go before you look at the answers at the end of the chapter. It *is* possible to form a cube out of a straight strip of squares but only if there are seven squares in the strip. The diagram on the next page shows how this is done.

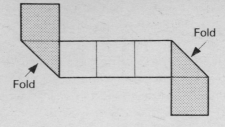

If one side of the strip is shaded and it contains eight squares it is possible to fold the strip into a cube so that only the shaded side is showing. See if you can sort out how that is done. (The solution is at the end of the chapter.)

With eight small cubes you can pile them up to make a larger cube which is really two cubes high, two cubes wide and two cubes deep.

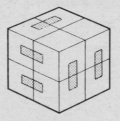

By taping the eight cubes together in the special way shown you can produce a flexicube. Your flexicube can be folded and folded and folded in a continuous moving loop until it drops apart or you go right round the bend. The whole thing can be made from building blocks or square boxes or you can make the cubes yourself.

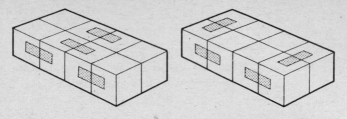

Here is a plan which shows how a flexicube can be made from one piece of paper. Use stiff paper, or better still, thin card. When you have finished you can draw different designs on the faces of the cubes and see how the patterns change when the cube is flexed.

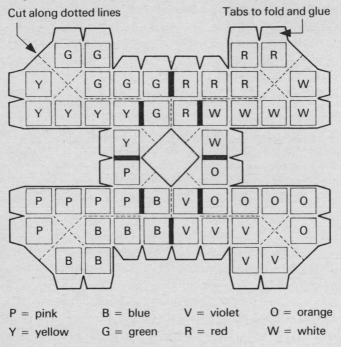

Cut along dotted lines

Tabs to fold and glue

| P = pink | B = blue | V = violet | O = orange |
| Y = yellow | G = green | R = red | W = white |

▌ Cube connecting edges

This flexicube is made from a piece of paper that is 8 squares deep and 10 squares wide, not counting tabs. However, it is possible to make a flexicube map that is only 6 squares deep and 10 squares wide. You may like to try to discover it. (Here's a tip: in every flexicube map, the eight edges that join the different cubes together need never change position.)

If you get so far as to make your own flexicube, you may find that you are suddenly hooked on cubes. That's what happened to me and it resulted in me thinking about flexicubes and comparing them with the Rubik Cube. Suddenly I began to wonder if it was possible to make a flexicube that contained 27 basic cubes and that could flex itself into the $3 \times 3 \times 3$ array of the Rubik Cube. This is what I came up with. I have called it the Fantastic Flexi-Rube. (I also call it a Rubi-Flex and I can't decide which name I like best.)

The Fantastic Flexi-Rube... or Rubi-Flex!

You are going to need 27 cubes to make the Flexi-Rube and I suggest you find some small kiddy blocks for the job. You will also need some sticky tape – I find that a roll of parcel tape works best.

First take the cubes three at a time and wrap them in tape as shown below. You will notice how the three blocks flex although fastened together.

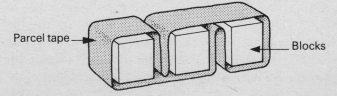

Parcel tape →

Blocks →

Next take three of these groups of three and wrap them to form a 3 × 3 square. This square should then flex in a similar way in two different directions. Repeat this with the other blocks until you have three squares of nine. Join the three squares up as shown below, and there is your Flexi-Rube or Rubi-Flex. (The diagram shows you how to tape the blocks together simply.)

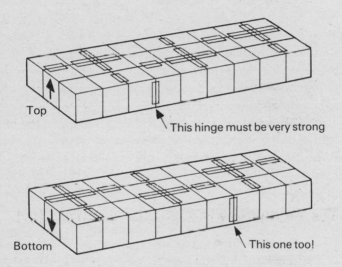

OK, so what can you do with your Rubi-Flex . . . or was it Flexi-Rube? Well, you can form four different 3 × 3 × 3 cubes. In each case the sides are different and there is a different centre cube in each case. In the original flat layout (above) there is one face and one face only on each side that is never seen when a cube has been formed. Can you find that face? (It's not the centre one.) Can you find the four cubes that each take up the centre position? Each cube has six faces and nine of the cubes show every face in one or other of the four 3 × 3 × 3 cubes. The diagram below shows how one of the cubes is formed.

If you cover your model in white paper (sticky labels would do) you can then draw different designs on the cubes to produce varying patterns. Perhaps the most exciting thing about the Rubi-Flex (sorry, Flexi-Rube) is that it will form many other shapes: the Wall, the Steps, the Cornerpiece, the Snake, the Monster, Diamonds, the Oil Rig and many, many more.

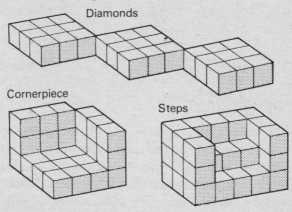

Diamonds

Cornerpiece

Steps

Monster

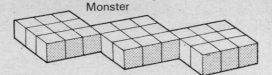

Snake

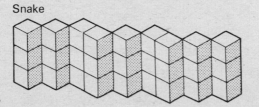

Wall

Oil rig

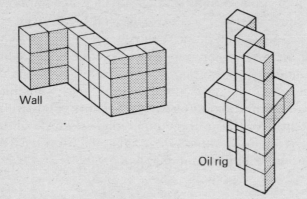

The octahedron

Apart from the cube, the most widely used form of die is the octahedron. Octahedral dice, however, don't roll as well as cubic dice. They tend to bungle along and give the impression that the shape is not regular. They can be numbered so that opposite sides add up to 7, just as with cubic dice, but this means putting o on one face and 7 on the opposite face.

Octahedrons can be made from strips of eight equilateral triangles but, once again, this cannot be done if the triangles form a straight line. However, with ten triangles in a straight line you *can* make an octahedron, and with twelve triangles in a straight line, you can form an octahedron with the same side of the paper showing all round.

Here is a grid from which you can make an octahedron. This is well worth making because by fitting a small elastic band as shown, the octahedron will squash flat and when released it will pop up into its three dimensional shape. You will need stiffish card for your octahedron to work well.

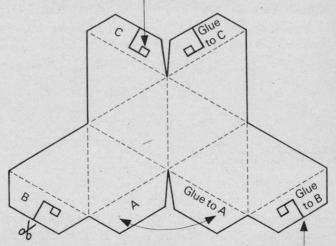

These are holes in which the elastic bands go

Slit to put the elastic band through

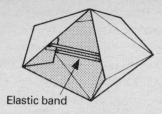

Elastic band

If you enjoyed the puzzle of finding the eleven grids that make up a cube, here again there are eleven grids of triangles that can be folded to produce an octahedron. See if you can find them. All but two of them can be formed using four diamonds made up of two triangles each. (The answers are at the end of the chapter.)

The dodecahedron

The dodecahedron is made up of twelve faces and it is different from the other platonic solids in that each face is a regular pentagon having five sides. The easiest way to make a pentagon is to take a strip of paper and tie a knot in it.

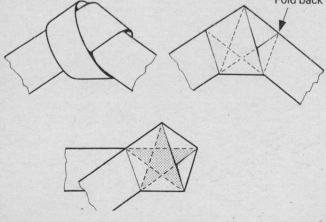

Fold back

You need to fold this shape carefully, pushing the ends through gradually as you tighten and flatten the knot. Then you can fold the ends over to produce the penta-gon. If you hold it up to a strong light, you will be able to see a five-pointed star or pentagram contained with-in the pentagon.

To make a dodecahedron you first need to know something about the measurements of a pentagon. There are only two basic measurements involved in a pentagon; the length of the side and the distance from one point to one of the further points. As it happens (I'm beginning to sound like Jimmy Savile), the re-lationship between these two measurements is always the same no matter what size you make your pentagon. Dividing the shorter length into the longer length will always give you the answer 1·618, and dividing the longer length into the shorter length will always give you the answer 0·618. This relationship between the two lengths is known as *the golden ratio* and will help you considerably when you are constructing pentagons or the more complicated shapes that form the pop-up dodecahedron.

How the dodecahedron measures up

In twelfth-century Pisa in Italy, there was a mathematician called Fibonacci. (The Leaning Tower was being built at that time but he had nothing to do with it. A mathematician wouldn't have built a crooked tower.) Fibonacci introduced zero to Europe, but he is more famous for the Fibonacci Series. This is a sequence of numbers which provides a great way of finding the ideal dimensions for making a pop-up dodecahedron. The series is made by adding consecutive numbers together.

0 1 1 2 3 5 8 13 21 34 55 89, etc.

Any two consecutive numbers, apart from the first few in the series, will, when divided by each other, always give the same answer. For instance, $8 \times 1\cdot618 = 12\cdot944$, which is very close to 13, so let's use 8cm $\times$ 13cm as our dimensions.

First take a piece of strong card that is more than 13cm square. Half of 13 is 6½, so start by marking a faint centre line parallel with the right-hand edge of the card and 6½cm away from it. From the point where this line touches the base line, mark off two points 4cm away on each side. This gives you a base line 8cm long labelled AB. Now draw a line 8cm long which joins B to the right-hand side of the card at C. Form the third side of the figure by drawing a line 8cm long from point C to the centre line at D. Join D to A and B. This will produce a tall, narrow isosceles triangle. Mark two points on the sides of the triangle which are both 8cm from A and B and label them E and F. You can now draw a line 13cm long which is parallel with the base

line and passes from C through the points F and E to G.
You can then complete the large pentagon by joining G
to D and G to A. Cut out the finished pentagon.

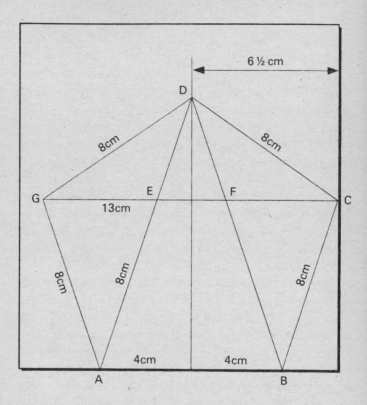

Join each corner point with each other corner point
in your pentagon (A to C, B to G, etc.). You will now see
a smaller inverted pentagon (dotted outline in diagram
opposite) in the centre of the large pentagon. By lining
up your ruler through the opposite points in the small
pentagon, you can mark out five triangles that will have

to be cut out of your large pentagon. Finally, score along the dotted lines in the small pentagon.

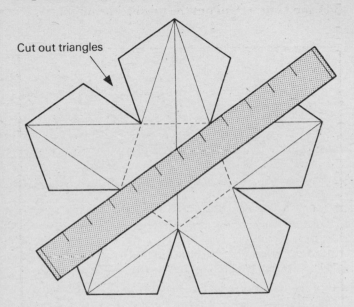

Cut out triangles

When you have done all this trace round the shape you have made and make another in the same thick card. This time it will be much easier. In fact, with patience the whole thing will prove quite straightforward and I'm sure you'll find the result well worthwhile.

Lay your two shapes on top of each other at an angle and then weave a rubber band around the points so that it holds the two shapes together by gripping all ten corners.

Rubber band

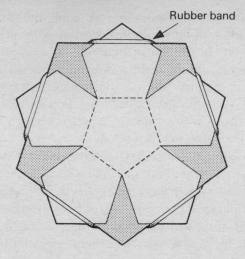

Providing the elastic band is tight enough, as you release the shape it automatically pops up to form a three-dimensional dodecahedron. Keep it under a pile of books and each time the books are removed it will delight everyone by popping up.

Besides being fascinating to look at, the dode-cahedron has a very important geometric role to play, such as in the design of footballs. If you examine a football you will see that it is made up of panels that usually come in two or sometimes three different shapes. Although some of the panels may be six-sided or even three- or four-sided, you will most certainly find some panels that are five-sided.

Here is a question that would probably fool most professional footballers even though they are kicking footballs every day. How many five sided panels has a football? The answer is twelve. This is because a foot-ball is a spherical object and the twelve five-sided panels help the other panels to come together to form a sphere. With only hexagonal panels the surface of the ball wouldn't curve at all, so the most important panels are the twelve five-sided ones and you can now see that footballs are modelled on the shape of the dode-cahedron.

The icosahedron

The incredible icosahedron is formed by twenty equilateral triangles. As I mentioned earlier, you can form this shape by using twenty tetrahedrons, but gathering them and then holding them together proves to be quite a juggling feat.

An icosahedron can be made from a grid of triangles (see next page).

However, there is another way of making an icosa-hedron and once again it involves the use of the golden ratio. This time you need three golden-ratio rectangles

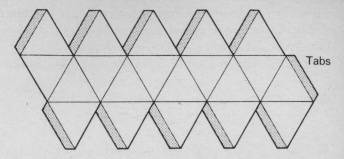

Tabs

made of strong card. Using numbers from the Fibonacci Series, I suggest you make the rectangles 13cm × 21cm. Make cuts 13cm long in the middle of two cards. On the third card the cut must be taken right through one side of the card.

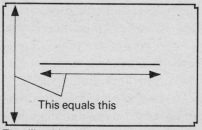

One like this

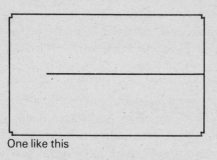

This equals this

Two like this

Cut out a small notch from each corner of the three cards as shown on the previous page. When that is done the cards can be slotted together as shown.

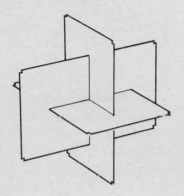

This shape can be used to explain the connections between a dodecahedron and an icosahedron. The dodecahedron has twelve faces and twenty points, but the icosahedron has twenty faces and twelve points. The shape formed by the three cards could form the support-structure for an icosahedron where the corners of one shape match the corners of the other.

To explain this, take a good length of coloured string or thread and fasten one end to a corner of the three card shape. Now carefully pass the string from corner to corner until every corner is connected to all the corners that surround it. The end result is an icosahedron formed by twenty triangles made up of string and the short edges of the three cards. (If patterned and coloured, these shapes make fabulous Christmas decorations.)

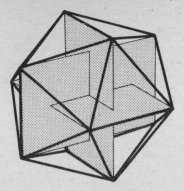

If you get really hooked on making geometric solids, then there is plenty of scope for making further models. Although there are only five platonic solids, there are thirteen Archimedian solids, not counting an infinite number of simple prisms; and then there are fifty-three additional uniform polyhedra!!! Don't worry if you don't know what that means. Here is a model of one of them. It's called a ditrigonal dodecahedron and making it is a bit of a problem!

Answers

Here are the eleven possible layouts which fold to make a cube. Any others you find will really be mirror reflections of these:

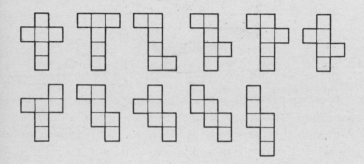

This diagram shows how to fold a cube from a straight strip of eight squares so that only one side of the paper is showing:

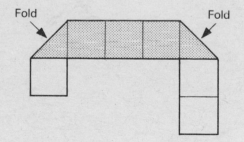

These are the eleven grids that fold to make an octahedron.

CHAPTER 11

Things to make you think

This book is full of things to make and things to practise and perform, but this chapter features a few things that may just make you *think*. The answers to the seven problems posed here can be found at the end of the chapter.

Problems

1 One square too many

First mark out an 8 × 8 array of squares. You should end up with a pattern like a chess board having 64 squares. Divide the pattern into four pieces using three cuts as shown below.

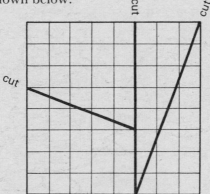

Now you can arrange the pieces to form a shape 13 squares long and 5 squares wide. But hang on, 5 × 13 = 65. You've got one more square than you started with. Where on earth did it come from? Before you look at the answer, examine the four pieces carefully and see if you can work out the secret for yourself.

2 The monk's journey

Monks can be found in many countries in the world, often living in isolated places with very few modern conveniences like pocket calculators or computers. The age of the micro-chip monk has not yet arrived. Having lots of time to devote to meditation, a mathematically minded monk might find the following problem worthy of some deep thought.

A monk decided to visit a neighbouring monastery which was some miles away at the top of a fairly large mountain. He set off at dawn and slowly began to climb the narrow path that led to the top and his destination. He took his time, often stopping to admire the view and he eventually arrived at the monastery just as the sun set over the distant hills. He dined with the resident monks and slept rather late the next morning. After saying goodbye, he set out down the mountain again, leaving at about 10.30. This time he made the journey at a steady jog trot and arrived home at 3.15 in the afternoon.

Here is the question. What were the chances of the monk being in exactly the same spot on the path at exactly the same time on the two journeys?

3 Scrumpled sheets

For this experiment you need two identical sheets of paper which need to be printed so that exact spots on the sheets can be identified. Identical sheets from two copies of the same daily paper would be ideal.

Place one sheet flat on a table and then place the second sheet directly over it. Every identical point on the two sheets should be exactly in line vertically.

Now scrumple up the top sheet as much as you like, but don't tear it. Leave it lying on top of the flat sheet.

Here is the question. What are the chances that two identical points on the sheets will still be exactly in line vertically?

4 The hitch-hiker's dream

The scene was an airport. A young girl was sitting on her suitcase, crying bitterly. A smart young man who happened to be passing stopped and said, 'I say, can I help you?' 'I wish you could,' said the girl, brushing away a tear, 'but no one can help me. I'm afraid I've lost my handbag containing my air ticket and all my money, so I can't get home.'

'Fear not, old girl,' said the young man, who looked quite nice but talked like a twit. 'My rich daddy bought me an aeroplane of my very own so I can drop you off.'

'But you don't know where I'm going,' said the girl.

'Oh, that doesn't matter, old fruit,' said the young man as he wound the string on his diamond-studded yo-yo. 'You see, where I'm going I can drop you off without going out of my way!'

Question: Where on earth was he going? (If it's any help, there are two possible answers.)

5 Ring round the world

The distance round the Earth over the Poles is very close to 40,000km (25,000 miles). Assuming that the Earth is perfectly round, the diameter (distance through the centre) would be:

40,000 ÷ pi (3·1416) = 12,732km (7957 miles)

A cable firm was asked to lay a cable round the Earth over the Poles and when they completed the job and brought the two ends together they found that they had just 12 metres (39ft) of cable too much. Instead of cutting off the 12 metres, the foreman suggested that the whole cable could be propped up a little distance above the Earth all the way round to take up the slack. For some idiotic reason that I won't go into, everyone agreed that this was the best thing to do, especially as 12 metres in a cable of 40,000,000 metres doesn't seem much at all, does it?

Question: If the slack is taken up by propping up the cable above the surface of the Earth by the same distance all the way round the Earth, how high would the props need to be?

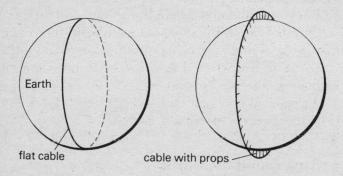

Earth

flat cable

cable with props

6 Needles with a point

Pi has a habit of cropping up in all kinds of unlikely places. Pi is the ratio of the circumference of a circle to its diameter. Usually, pi is given the value of $3\frac{1}{7}$ or $3\cdot1416$, although a couple of French mathematicians worked out pi to 1,000,000 decimal places.

In the eighteenth century another Frenchman, George Louis, Comte de Buffon, used to pass the time dropping needles onto the floorboards in his room and counting the number of times the needles came to rest on the cracks between the boards. Why not try the experiment yourself and see if you come up with the same answers that he did? Buffon used needles, but a box of pins would probably be more readily available and safer.

Get a sheet of paper and rule across it a series of parallel lines spaced the length of a pin apart.

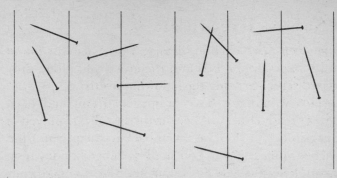

Now drop the pins at random onto the paper. Record the number of pins dropped and also the number of pins that land crossing or touching a line. Make a table like the one below and see if you come up with the same results.

No. of drops	No. touching lines (approx)
10	6
32	20
100	64
157	100
377	240

Question: Can you work out what the results have to do with pi and why?

AAHHHH!

7 No noose is good noose

A few centuries back in history, a prisoner was found guilty of stealing a loaf and the crusty old judge duly passed sentence using the following words:

'This would not have happened if you had been better bread. However, because of the roll you played in this crime, you shall be taken back to the prison from whence you came and you shall be hanged at dawn on one of the next seven days. Furthermore, to make your suffering worse, you will not know beforehand which day the hanging will take place. Take him away.'

The guards rose to lead the prisoner out, but the unfortunate wretch suddenly began to smile and then burst into fits of laughter.

'Pray, what do you find funny?' asked the judge.

'Funny? It's hysterical,' said the prisoner. 'Because of what you've just said, I cannot be hanged next week. I'm saved, saved!'

Question: Was he saved, and if so, how?

Answers

1 The solution to this problem is difficult to sort out unless you make your original 8 × 8 array very accurately. When you rearrange the pieces to form a 5 × 13 array you should notice that they don't fit quite as neatly as they should. In actual fact, the pieces don't fit together at all. The diagram here shows what really happens.

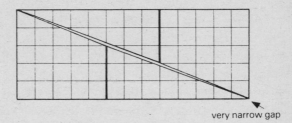

very narrow gap

In the 5 × 13 array there is a long thin space diagonally across the array. Although it's very thin the area of this shape should work out at the same as the area of one square so that the pieces still cover an area of 64 squares.

2 The best way to explain the monk's journey is to imagine two monks making two journeys, one up and one down the mountain on the same day. They must pass at some time and so it is a certainty that at some particular moment they must be at the same point on the journey.

3 This problem is very similar to the previous one, but much harder to believe. Provided the scrumpled sheet is totally over the flat sheet there is always one pair of

points that are still in line although it may be difficult to trace the actual points.

4 I think this is a beautiful problem because you are given so little information. You don't know where on earth they are or where the girl is going. There are only two possible places that the pilot can be going to. Either he is going to a spot on exactly the opposite side of the world, or he is going right round the world and coming back to the same place. In either case, it doesn't matter which way he goes. If he keeps straight on he will reach his destination. Once the girl tells him where she is going he can head that way, drop her off and then continue his journey without going out of his way.

5 This problem is quite mathematical, but worth tackling because of the amazing answer. To get the diameter of the Earth, you divide the circumference (distance round the Earth) by pi. By adding 12m, you are increasing the circumference by that amount. Thus the diameter will increase by 12m divided by pi.

$$12 \div 3{\cdot}1416 = 3{\cdot}82\text{m}$$

This new diameter will stick out from the surface of the Earth by half that distance on each side so the props needed all round the Earth will be 3·82m ÷ 2 = 1·91m (approx. 6ft 3in). Doesn't seem possible, does it?

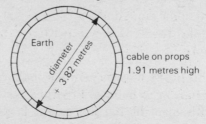

Earth

diameter + 3.82 metres

cable on props
1.91 metres high

6   The Comte de Buffon found that the answer to this problem always tended towards twice the number of drops divided by pi.

No. of drops	Multiplied by 2	Divided by pi	Equals	Approx.
10 × 2 = 20		÷ 3·1416 =	6·366	6
32	64		20·37	20
100	200		63·66	64
157	314		99·95	100
377	754		240·445	240

Why does it work this way? The simple explanation is that the pins can come to rest pointing in any direction. If you take the centre of a fallen pin as a point of reference, all the possible positions of that pin would together form a circle round that point. Thus, pi and circular mathematics are essential in calculating the number of pins likely to fall on a line.

7   The reason for the prisoner's happiness was his understanding of what the judge had said. He stipulated that the prisoner would not know beforehand the day on which he was to be hanged. Working backwards from the end of the next week, the prisoner deduced that they could not possibly hang him on the last day because he would know about it just after dawn the day before and the judge had said he was not to know in advance.

If he can't be hanged on the last day of the week, what about the next to last day? Well, they can't hang him on that day because he would know that was to be the day just after dawn on the day before. So the prisoner can't be hanged on the last two days. What about the third from last day? The same thing applies, and using this train of thought, the prisoner was able to eliminate every single day in the week as a hanging day.

This is a paradoxical situation. (A paradox is something self-contradicting, not two web-footed quacking birds!) So, what happened to the prisoner? Dunno . . . they probably shot him.

INDEX

Adding from 1 to 100 18
All-over pattern 70

Base Ten System 13
Base Three System 16
Billion-pound brain 82
Binary system 15
Brilliant bibliographical
    brain 80

Card tricks 27
    As many as you . . . 28
    Four-suit swindle 30
    Magic square 32
    *Red and black, red and black
    29*
    Six-card trick 35
    Wrong way up 31
Chinese abacus 14
Choose an object 55
Coins on a clock face 53
Cube 127, 145
Curious course of a curve 106
Curious curves 71

Diabolical magic square 86
Dice, to make with pencils
    119
Digital root 93
Ditrigonal dodecahedron 144

Division 20
Do you remember the day
    you were born? 95
Dodecahedron 135, 137

Elizabethan multiplication 23
Ellipse 73
Ellipse-shaped billiard table
    75
Extraordinary coincidence 93

Fibonacci series 137
Flexicube 128
Flexicube map 129
Flexi-Rube (or Rubi-Flex)
    130
Four-dice trick 59

Gauss, Karl Friedrich 18
Geometric solids 122
Getting in a twist 65
Golden ratio 136
Guess your age 91

Hexahedron 127
Hexahexaflexagon 46
Hexatetraflexagon 44
Hitch-hiker's dream 149
How big is a hole? 62

Icosahedron 141

Jumping elastic bands 111

Lewis Carroll's
    elliptical-wheeled cart 76

Maddening months 94
Maggie and Ronnie
    coincidence explained
    102
Magical matrix 84
Mammoth dice trick 118
Match tricks 51, 122
Möbius Band 38
Monk's journey 148
Multiplying by nine 13

Needles with a point 151
Nine-Day Wonder 99
No noose is good noose 153
Number patterns 24
Number tricks 79

Octahedron 133, 146
One-day-per-week trick 98
One square too many 147

Pair-picking time 81
Paper clip linking 115
Paper curling 37

Paper plane 61
Paper tearing 104
Parabolic curves 72
Pentagon 135
Plaiting game 68
Plaiting paper 65
Platonic solids 123
Playing cards, origin of 27

Quadrilateral patterns 70

Rather crooked rope trick 108
Ring round the world 150
Russian multiplication 21

Scrumpled sheets 149
Single selection of a
    supersensory signal 103
Simple addition 11

Tertiary system 16
Tetratetraflexagon 42
Tetrahedron 124
Think of a number with dice
    117
Three-object divination 56
Three piles of matches (or
    paper clips) 51
Time-keeping 89
Time-tapping 90
Tricks with dice 116